THE Safety Minute

THE Safety Minute:01

Living on High Alert; How to take control of your personal security and prevent fraud.

by ROBERT L. SICILIANO

Foreword by Charles Andrews CPP, CCPS*

BOSTON, MASSACHUSETTS

Safety Zone PRESS

*CPP - Certified Protection Professional; CCPS - Certified Crime Prevention Specialist

THE Safety Minute : 01

Living on High Alert; How to take control
of your personal security and prevent fraud.

by Robert L. Siciliano

Published by:

Safety Zone PRESS

P.O. Box 15145
Boston MA 02215

This is a completely updated version of *The Safety Minute: How to be safe in the streets, at home, and abroad so you can save your life!* copyrighted 1996

Disclaimer...

Editor: Chris Roerden
Illustrator: Ken Tango
Cover Design: V Van Sant - *Off the Mac Design*

PRINTED IN THE UNITED STATES OF AMERICA

Publishers Cataloging in Publication

Siciliano, Robert L.
The safety minute: living on high alert; how to take control of your personal security and prevent fraud. / Robert L Siciliano.

    p. cm.
    Includes index
    ISBN 0-9648126-7-3..: 19.95

    1. Crime prevention   2. Self defense I. Title.

HV7431.S565 2003   613.6
                QBI03-200245

Dedication

To all who have, unfortunately, become a statistic of some sort. Your painful experience was not all a waste.

As we develop as a society, we learn from the good and the bad. Your experience will some day come to save the life of someone who is loved.

The above LCD one-minute symbol represents 60 seconds of positive or negative life energy.

One minute can represent the difference between life and death in your personal security.

If we "take a minute" to ensure our personal security before leaving our homes every day, how much safer would we be?

If we took "just a minute" to be courteous to another person, how much joy could we spread?

If we "live every minute" geared toward giving to others and learning for ourselves, what kind of world would we live in?

Minute by minute, the FBI crime clock ticks away its victims.

Every minute new people are born and other people die.

A minute has passed since you started to read this book. Have you grown?

What can you contribute in the next minute to make a better world?

It takes only a minute to change a life.

Contents

List of Illustrations

Acknowledgments

This book was made possible only through the love and compassion I have received from the many wonderful people in my network of professional colleagues, friends, and, most important, my family.

My family Bob, Judi, Michael, Lou, Gino, Gayle and Katie. Thank you for helping me to grow. My family is the foundation on which I have built my life. Thanks for sharing, caring, and loving.

To Maureen, my S.O. and my biggest fan. You energize me, support me and inspire me. I'm a better person because of you.

My amazing editor, Chris Roerden. If anyone wants a quality editor who has a big beautiful heart, Chris is the one. You receive full credit for the easy readability of this book.

To my graphic designer, Vicki V. You are an eternal friend who has been there since day one. Your creativity and insight continue to add color to my life. Thank you so much.

All the wonderful people from the National Speakers Association have assisted me in my most consistent professional growth.

Of course I'd like to thank my clients, without whom I would have neither an audience nor the pleasure of being involved in such a wonderful, rewarding career as this.

Finally, I'd like to thank all the women who have come into my life and confided in me the pain that they have endured in their struggle for peace and security. I have been deeply affected by your pain. I live my life with you in mind, constantly working at making a safer world for you to live in.

To each and every one of you, I wish you continued success. Thank you for making this life such a wonderful experience.

—Robert L. Siciliano

"THE LIFESAVER"

A personal note to the reader

As I was growing up, I was faced with numerous confrontations—for reasons only kids know. As luck would have it, my enemies were always twice my size, so I was forced to learn how to protect myself. I joined a karate school where I learned basic self-defense techniques. I learned kick boxing, which taught me how to bring together all the other techniques. And I learned Model Mugging, which gave me some badly needed courage to defend myself.

When I began to date, I discovered that men are not the only gender that must know how to fight. I was shocked to learn from the women I dated that nearly half of them had been raped. While I felt grateful that these women trusted me enough to share such a painful and intimate experience of their lives, I was enraged that our society accepted—and continues to accept—such physical violation as commonplace.

Compelled to do something about my outrage, I decided to start my own company for the primary purpose of teaching both men and women how to avoid and escape assault. To reach even more people with this information, I have written *The Safety Minute*.

In our ever-changing world, I have noticed one significant thing about people. Overall, people are good. Sometimes too good and too trusting. Because there is an element of society in which individuals prey upon others for their own benefit, I have tried to compile as much information as I could to keep all you trusting people from getting duped. Scams and fraud are more prevalent now than ever. The Internet and other technological advances have brought upon us a whole new level of theft that would make a snake oil salesman proud.

Everyone I teach is a special person. You are special. If I can make your life safer with even one tip, I've done my job. Please pass on the information you learn from reading this book to the people you care about.

What you pass on, you will keep forever. I wish you peace, love, and happiness.

—*Robert L. Siciliano*
"THE LIFESAVER"

NOTE: Although attackers come in both genders, I refer to them in this book by the male pronoun because the overwhelming number of them are male.

Foreword

by Charles E. "Chuck" Andrews, CPP, CCPS

If experience counts for anything—and in the law enforcement field it counts big time—then my comments on Robert L. Siciliano's incredible book, *The Safety Minute,* will hit home.

My love of law enforcement began when I was 13 and an Explorer Scout in a small Texas town. For six years I rode "shotgun" with the hometown police officers, working days, nights, and even graveyards to learn everything I could. From here my lifelong commitment to crime prevention began.

In school I came across these words of Sir Robert Peel, and they established a philosophy for my commitment. Considered the father of law enforcement, Peel set the standard for policing in London. He wrote, "The citizens are the police, and the police are the citizens. First and foremost, it shall be the commission of all police officers to *prevent crime!*"

Somehow in America we have lost the spirit of Peel's philosophy. Instead, police work is frequently reactive. Dispatching an officer after a crime has occurred only creates a statistic which supposedly measures a police department's success or failure. The reactive mode is "business as usual"—but there *is* another way.

Community policing gets officers out of cars and puts them on foot or on bicycles to work more closely with citizens. The theory is solid. Nevertheless, across the country implementation is slow. Few communities are successfully practicing community policing.

Citizen involvement, which lies at the heart of community

policing, is the answer. Whether it's in the Reserve Police Officers, Junior Police, Police Explorers, Neighborhood Watch, Community Watch, Crime Stoppers, Citizen Police Academies, Senior Citizen Watch, Police Athletic Leagues, Police Review Boards, or Crime Forums—getting the community involved in crime prevention is what makes the difference.

Because I work in the crime prevention section of law enforcement, I know that prevention, involvement, communication, and ownership are the keys to reducing crime. The emotional damage of being victimized by a crime leaves lifetime scars. Every victim of a crime I've ever met wishes he or she could turn back the clock. Please don't find yourself wishing the same wish.

After 19 years of experience—in crime prevention for a police agency in the Denver–Metro area of Colorado and in owning my own crime prevention consulting business—I have pursued, implemented, and developed every crime prevention program imaginable for my community.

I have been highly successful in my work by spreading the "good news" about crime prevention using an "Andy of Mayberry" public relations campaign. As a result, the community has benefited tremendously.

However, none of us can afford to depend solely on the police for protection. Citizens must be prepared to defend themselves, their families, friends, community, property, and way of life. To that end, I wholeheartedly endorse the one book that has everything ordinary citizens should know to do—in one minute's time—to prevent or survive an attack: *The Safety Minute!*

My friend and colleague, Robert L. Siciliano, has written this wonderful book to do exactly that. A remarkable individual, Robert has dedicated his life to making sure people live a safe life. His ten tips are detailed, yet simple, and his one-minute philosophy is relevant for staying safe in every aspect of life—physical and mental.

After reading this book you will conclude, as I have, that Robert has written the best lifesaving tool available on the market. No longer do we need to rely on the "red light" theory in which we wait for a fatal crash to occur before installing a light at the intersection. *The Safety Minute* gives you defensive-driving lessons in one minute that will raise your consciousness and possibly save your life.

Once you read this book, you will be compelled to share it with family, friends, and co-workers. Thanks, Robert, for a job well done. *The Safety Minute* is a tremendous contribution. God Bless and keep up the good work!

Charles E. Andrews, CPP, CCPS, has received numerous awards recognizing his crime prevention successes. The most prestigious was given to him by the International Society of Crime Prevention Practitioners in 1992 at its International Conference in Washington. This was the same year Chuck was selected for the lifetime award known as the George B. Sunderland Award, a one-time award for Crime Prevention programming and dedication recognizing his career of practicing crime prevention. He is the youngest person to ever receive this award.

In addition, Chuck was selected as the Crime Prevention Officer and Unit of the year in the State of Colorado. He also received citations from the Governor of Colorado, the Veterans of Foreign Wars, the Drug Enforcement Administration, the Optimist Club, the Chamber of Commerce, and many others.

A mind once stretched by a new idea
never regains its original dimensions.

:01

Chapter 1
Take a Minute for Safety

"For the first time in our nation's culture, the wilderness is safer than civilization."

—Faith Popcorn

Take a Minute for Safety

"Hey Siciliano, what are you, some kind of a fairy?" says this overgrown Cro-Magnon Mickey the Dunce.

I respond, "No, what's wrong, didn't your mother give you enough attention growing up?"

BAM! I get whacked upside the head. I respond with a palm heel to the chin, sending him into la-la land for the next minute and giving the spectators enough time to break up the fight.

I believe he was intimidated by the fact that I was well groomed and nicely dressed, and was dating the best-looking girl in town. (Since that day I have bounced many underdeveloped subspecies just like him.)

The next day I'm walking home by myself on a busy main street and start to get a queasy feeling in my stomach. I turn to my right and see an old beat-up tan Chevy Chevelle skidding in my direction. Five cavemen jump out and surround me. As I freeze with fear they start to pummel me to the ground, kicking, punching, and spitting on me until they feel I have paid.

When I stand up all bloody, reeking of my own waste, I see a cop 30 feet away from the scene standing and watching. Whose responsibility was my safety?

The answer: Mine.

Once we take full responsibility for everything in our lives, that's when living begins.

Most Americans believe that their local police have a duty to protect them against criminals. Wrong. A police officer's primary job is to preserve the peace by apprehending a criminal after a crime has been committed.

Of course, part of the job of the police is to remove the opportunity to commit crime, and to this end police officers patrol the streets, advise citizens on security, and apprehend perpetrators so they don't have the chance to commit more crimes. But the police do not have a duty to protect the public before a crime is committed. In fact, there have been cases in which police officers have promised to protect a potential victim and failed to do so. When the victims later sued the police department, they lost.

The lesson here is that the responsibility for your personal security rests on your own shoulders. You can't expect the police to do it for you. Although you are not "guilty" of having provoked an attack, you are in the best position to prevent one.

Take a minute to participate in a simple self-assessment. Your answers will tell you what you need to do to make yourself safer.

Take-a-Minute Self-Assessment

1. When you walk, do you daydream, stare at the ground, or carry your purse loosely?
2. Are you a passive, obedient, cooperative person?
3. Do you consider yourself weak or frail?
4. When someone looks you in the eye, do you blush or look away?
5. If the food you are served in a restaurant is cold or poorly prepared, do you keep silent so as not to cause trouble?
6. Do you become fearful if someone gives you a mean look or raises his voice to you? Do you feel afraid when home alone?
7. When you feel fear, do you become weak and paralyzed?

8. Do you think that crime or violence can't happen to you? That it happens only to other people?
9. When your instincts tell you that something is wrong, do you ignore your feelings or try to rationalize them?
10. Do you have a hard time saying "No" to people?
11. Is there anyone in your life who does not respect your attitudes or moral choices? Is there anyone with whom you are constantly uncomfortable? Is this person in your life daily?
12. Do you try not to think about crime?
13. Do you use alcohol or drugs? Even occasionally?
14. Is your life very routine? Do you walk the same streets, take the same bus routes, always bank on Fridays, always buy groceries on Saturday mornings, and so on?
15. Do you wear a lot of jewelry? Do you carry a lot of cash or many credit cards?
16. Do you wear very high heels, tight pants or skirts, or other styles of clothing that would make it difficult for you to run or defend yourself?
17. Do you give directions or the time of day to anyone who asks?
18. If you were attacked, would you just freeze up and let it happen?

If you answer "yes" to any of these questions, you must actively work to change your attitudes and take positive steps to incorporate safe behavior into your life.

As a security consultant for many years, I have taught thousands of people of every age and physical condition how to protect themselves. Whatever your strength or age, you can easily lower your risk of becoming a crime victim simply by employing the techniques outlined on the following pages.

First, you must learn to be aware of your surroundings. Then you must learn how to project the right attitude. Finally, you must learn how to protect yourself if you should ever be attacked.

ATTACKERS AVOID	ATTACKERS PREY ON
Alertness	Daydreaming
Assertiveness	Passivity
Strength	Frailty
Eye contact	Helpless eyes
Confidence	Self-doubt
Decisiveness	Indecisiveness
Sobriety	Intoxication
Conservative dress	Gaudy, flashy dress
Flexibility	Stiffness
Worldliness	Naïveté

Table 1.1. Attitude is Altitude: Take-a-Minute Self-Assessment

A good self-defense course such as Model Mugging teaches self-defense utilizing adrenal stress training. In this kind of training, after students learn basic self-defense techniques, they get the opportunity to use those techniques on a padded instructor who pretends to be an attacker. The "attacker" offends the student with verbal abuse, thereby creating an adrenalized state. Then the attacker lunges and attempts to disable the student as the student overcomes the padded attacker.

In the event of a real attack, the student experiences a rush of adrenaline and automatically associates that adrenalized state with what he or she learned in class.

What I have discovered over a period of time is that if you are in danger, there are many ways to defend yourself. In fact the only thing you can do wrong is to do *nothing*.

As long as you survive, you've done the right thing.

Over the years I've noticed that all victims have one thing in common: they aren't aware of what's going on around them. They fail to pay attention to their surroundings, thereby signaling to potential aggressors that they are easy targets.

Security experts agree that the best way to protect yourself is to avoid potentially dangerous situations. Criminals look for vulnerability—an "easy mark," so to speak. But even if you must be in a dangerous situation, a well-rehearsed plan of action can prevent you or your family from becoming victims.

Here are seven tips that can help keep you safer.

1. **Be aware.** Constant awareness of your environment is your best defense. Always be alert, whether you are in your car, on the street, or at home.

2. **Have a plan of action.** Play a mental "what if" game. Where would you go and what would you do should a dangerous situation occur?

3. **Trust your instincts.** Research shows that most assault victims had a feeling something was wrong just before they were attacked.

4. **Take notice** if an acquaintance is paying unwarranted attention to you. More than half of all assaults are committed by someone known to the victim.

5. **Keep your senses free.** Don't wear radio headphones, large hats, or other devices that make it difficult for you to sense an attacker. Be alert at all times.

6. **Yell "No!"** If someone accosts you, yell "No!" as loudly as you can. Don't yell "Help" or "Rape" because these words give the message: "I'm weak and helpless"—a message that attackers feed upon. "No!" is powerful. In fact, it has been proven that the word "No" is said to us hundreds of thousands of times in our lifetimes. When we hear "No," it actually causes a biochemical reaction in our bodies.

7. **Yell "I don't know this man!"** Let bystanders know that you do not know the assailant so they don't mistake the attack for a domestic quarrel.

This book teaches you these and many other Take-a-Minute-for-Safety tips for dealing with assault and preventing fraud. Study this information. Read and reread it until you absorb its ideas and also feel prepared physically and mentally to make your life safer and handle an assault if one should threaten you.

Myths

In every seminar I do, this question always comes up: "What do I do if there is a gun or a knife involved?"

In watching the news, you might think weapons are involved in most crimes. Actually, weapons are used in fewer than 5 percent of crime situations. This means that 95 percent of the time no weapon is involved. This does not mean that you approach every situation as if there were no weapon involved. You must still maintain an awareness of that 5 percent.

Let's say you are approached, and someone puts a gun to your back. If the attacker takes you to a "secondary crime scene"—that is, makes you get in a car, go into a building, or leave the spot where you are initially coerced—you are dead.

Suppose you decide against going to the secondary crime scene and taking your chances with the gun. Let's say you break free and start to run. There's a 50-50 chance the gunman will shoot. You just reduced the odds of being shot at by 50 percent. Further suppose that the gunman has a 50 percent likelihood of being accurate enough to hit his target. You have further reduced the odds of being hit to 25 percent. Let's say there's a 50-50 chance that the bullet that hits you creates a mortal wound. You have reduced your chances of being killed to 12.5 percent. That means you have an 87.5 percent chance of getting away with your life. Not bad odds.

You know that if you go to a secondary crime scene you are as good as dead. What's a potential victim to do? The actual statistic for being mortally wounded in an on-the-street confrontation is *only 2 percent.* You have a 98 percent chance of getting away.

Should you discover that a bullet is inevitable, grab the barrel of the gun and direct it away from you. In a life-and-death situation, you must forget the rules and play for keeps.

Knives are similar. If you must grab the blade to direct it away from your "kill zone"—that is, your stomach, chest, or head—you will probably get cut. Thirty stitches in the hand are better than six spikes in the casket.

Defending yourself against a knife or a gun is very possible. Dozens of books, videos, and classes are available that teach proven techniques for defending yourself against lethal weaponry. The information I'm providing here is only a snippet of what is available because video and hands-on are more effective than anything I could try to explain in print. I encourage you to contact me to learn more.

Attitude is Altitude.

**Personal security, like success in business,
is being on top of what is new and
ahead of what is next at all times.**

:01

Chapter 2
The 10 Types of Personal Safety

"Security is an illusion. Life is either a daring
adventure or it is nothing at all."

—Helen Keller

The 10 Types of Personal Safety

Every minute, the FBI crime clock* proclaims the victims:
- a workplace violence murder every 2 days
- a murder every 34 minutes
- an identity theft reported every 19 minutes
- a robbery every 43 seconds
- a car theft every 34 seconds
- an assault every 24 seconds
- a victim of a stalker every 20 seconds
- a burglary every 9 seconds
- a violent crime every 5 seconds
- a theft every 2 seconds
- a rape/assault on a woman 172 an hour

On average, 6 million violent crimes are committed annually, including a million robberies and 5 million assaults.

The cost to society is enormous. Crime and the expenses it entails cost victims an estimated $1.4 billion every year; everyone experiences the economic and social costs of 6.1 million workdays lost annually because of crime.

The 21st century has brought terrorism to U.S. soil. War in our own backyards. As frightening as this is, this isn't the first time in

*See http://www.fbi.gov/

U.S. history we have been faced with this kind of horror. We survived the Revolutionary War, the Civil War, Pearl Harbor, the bombing in Oklahoma, and a slew of terrorist attacks in our own schools by our own American children. Many people are murdered every year by their own disgruntled co-workers. One in four women will be raped in their lives. Eighty percent of all people will become victims of some form of theft.

Every crime listed above is done by a terrorist, a frightening enemy, an unknown, unseen enemy. One who lives among us hides within our society and suddenly strikes where and when we least expect it. When your child is stolen walking home from school, that's terror. Religious fanatics who blow themselves up are also terrorists.

People generally believe that "It can't happen to me" —that crime and terror happen to other people or in other countries. That's the head-in-the-sand mentality that got us where we are today.

We ask the questions, "What are the warning signs, who's at risk, and what are the likely areas to be targeted?" These are the questions that everyday Americans never asked themselves before 9-11. People are waking up. We are evolving into a safety and security mentality. It's about time. By reading this book you are taking responsibility for averting terror and reducing crime. Your Mom would be proud.

Take charge. Don't become a statistic.

If you have the attitude that "It can't happen to me," you will surely be a victim.

But if you prepare for the possibility of violent crime by memorizing and using the tips below, you will greatly increase your chances of avoiding or escaping assault. These tips cover 10 types of personal safety: on the streets, in your car, at home, while traveling on vacation, in hotels, in airports, when using public transit, on the telephone, dating, and raising children.

1. Safety on the streets

Anyone walking the streets alone, regardless of age or sex, is at risk of assault. But contrary to popular belief, street crime is not completely random in nature. Most people believe that they become victims because they are in the wrong place at the wrong time. The fact is that all of us have a great deal of control over whether or not we are chosen as victims.

How do you minimize the risk of assault on the street? The answer is to walk purposefully and confidently. A brisk self-confident manner sends potential assailants the message that you would put up a *major* fight if they tried to attack you.

Many professional counselors say that if you are a negative person, you attract negative situations and negative people into your life.

On the other hand, if you are a positive, healthy person, you attract positive people and situations. The same is true about your personal safety on the street. If you walk fearfully, you will attract a fearful situation. But if you walk with confidence, you'll repel a fearful situation simply because you don't look like an easy victim.

Walk quickly. Walk with the attitude that absolutely no one has the right to attack you. Keep your head up. Keep your shoulders back. Be alert to everything around you. This is not being paranoid. This is making full use of your natural, animal awareness. When the hair on the back of your neck stands up, it's a warning. Don't ignore it or hide from it. Use your animal instincts.

Listen. Then react.

Respond *immediately* to any danger. If you hear steps behind you, turn around quickly.

Those few seconds could keep someone from leaping toward you. If you think someone means to harm you, yell.

Be rude! A real estate agent once told me her motto is "Better rude than raped."

Make a scene!

Most people who escape an attack fight off their assailants in the first moments. Your sudden response can throw an attacker off guard and give you time to escape. The only woman who got away from serial killer Ted Bundy was also the one who fought back.

If someone lunges toward you or grabs you, say "No!" in a firm, loud voice. Use the voice you would use in disciplining a dog. Give a direct order that the assailant can follow.

Say "Turn around and leave me alone!" or "Keep going, buddy!"

Don't cry, beg, panic, or plead. Don't smile or laugh. Studies show that weaker responses not only fail to deter criminals but actually increase the severity of an assault.

Here are some points to remember when you walk alone.

1. Be alert and aware. Continually scan the area around you. Walk briskly, keep eyes and chin up, and listen for warning sounds.
2. Plan your schedule so you get to your destination in daylight.
3. Carry a flashlight if you are walking at night.
4. Choose a sensible and safe path to or from your car. Use well-lit, populated routes whenever possible.
5. Be ready to unlock your car without having to fumble for keys.
6. Avoid poorly lit areas and shortcuts where you are hidden from others. The presence of other people can help deter an attack; if you are assaulted or threatened, others can help you.
7. Don't appear lost or alone. Assailants often prey on people who seem to be unfamiliar with their surroundings. If you're walking in an area that you don't know, ask a store security guard

or police officer for detailed directions.

8. Be ready to react. Keep your hands free and wear sensible clothes and shoes that do not restrict your movement.

9. If you think someone is following you, change direction, cross the street, slow down, speed up, or go into stores.

10. If the person keeps following you, immediately ask for help. Ask a security guard to escort you to your car.

11. Don't assume that you are invincible or immune to assault. Never feel embarrassed or awkward about asking for help. Your safety is paramount!

12. If you use a weapon, carry it in your hand and be prepared to use it. Or look around for rocks, bottles, sticks, or clubs that you can use as weapons if necessary. Carry Mace® or pepper spray if your state or city allows it.

13. Carry 10 or 15 one-dollar bills in an easily accessible pocket. Then if someone tries to rob you, you can throw the "chump change" several feet away. The robber will scramble after it, giving you time to escape.

14. Keep your ID and other items containing your address in your pocket, not in a purse or wallet.

15. Carry only the cash, checks, or credit card you absolutely need.

16. Do not flaunt money or valuables. Do not wear excessive jewelry. Turn rings around to hide gems, and avoid wearing loose gold chains.

17. Don't use an outdoor automated teller machine at night or in unfamiliar or unsafe surroundings. Criminals know you are carrying cash at these times. In the event of trouble, use the ATM phone, if there is one, and ask the operator to call for assistance. At a drive-thru, keep all doors locked and windows up. Keep your receipts.

18. Be alert when leaving stores or shopping malls. Shopping time is prime robbery time. Criminals know that you are carrying

cash, checkbooks, credit cards, or valuable merchandise.

19. Stay alert! If someone moves inside your personal comfort zone, move away. If he persists, run. If necessary, strike him before he strikes you.

20. Do not use the stairwells in parking garages. Try walking down the auto ramp instead. As long as you watch for cars, the ramp is much safer.

21. Walk facing oncoming traffic. Walking against rather than

	Victim	Attacker
Stage 1: Physical & mental states	fear panic anger shock assertiveness helplessness shortness of breath	fear frustration anger passion intoxication insecurity shortness of breath
Stage 2: Actions, attitudes, intentions	No! No! No! escaping getting help aggressiveness submissiveness decisiveness fighting giving valuables	profanities grabbing assessing aggressiveness retreating committing murder/rape/robbery assaulting/abducting getting a fix
Stage 3: Methods/ results	shouting talking manipulating fighting tricking running faking sickness using weapon reversal	isolation intimidating injuring forcing tricking retreating using weapon tragedy defeat

Table 2.1. Typical Stages in Attack Situations.

with traffic reduces the risk that you will be followed, forced into a car, and abducted.

22. If someone in a car asks for directions, stay far enough away from the car so you can turn and run easily. Or simply say "I don't know" and keep walking.

23. When friends drop you off at home or work, ask them not to leave until you are safely inside the door. When you drop friends off, do the same for them.

24. If you are alone in an elevator and someone threatening gets on, quickly step out.

25. If you don't have time to get off, press as many buttons as you can and then get off at the first opportunity. Don't press the "stop" button because the elevator will stop, the doors will stay closed, and you'll be trapped.

26. Use extreme caution when you are approaching any unlighted entryway. A common tactic of criminals is to remove, unscrew, or break the light bulbs in such places.

27. Take a dog with you if you are walking alone.

Most of these points are simple common sense. But the most important one is to stay alert and express confidence with your body and voice.

Studies reveal that those who show fear with their voices or bodies and those who fail to stay alert are assaulted at least twice in their lifetimes.

Being a victim, believe it or not, is a choice.

---

2. Safety in your car

Automobiles are a magnet for criminals. They want the car, the contents, or the owner.

Like the average home, cars are easy to break into, easy to hide in, and easy to sabotage. Unlike your home, they can be transported and sold easily or stripped down for parts that can be sold.

Do all you want to prevent theft—alarms, wheel locks, etc.—these will prevent a joy rider from stealing your car but not a professional.

To protect yourself and your vehicle from predators on the streets, follow these six areas of automobile safety.

1. Keep your car well maintained.
2. Practice safe parking habits.
3. Change your behavior on the road.
4. Know how to handle emergency and police stops.
5. Avoid carjackers and kidnappers.
6. Know what to do on long-distance drives.

Keep your car well maintained

Keeping your vehicle in good running order lowers your chances of being in a dangerous situation. Routine maintenance and prompt replacement of worn parts will help significantly to prevent break-downs, especially breakdowns in dangerous or isolated areas where help is far away.

Think of routine, preventive maintenance as part of your investment in the automobile. You don't want your engine to fail in the middle of a blizzard or overheat on a lonely mountain road.

Get regular oil changes and fluid checks. Replace all four tires together instead of one at a time. Get new brakes *before* the old ones start to slip. Also equip your car with some simple safety tools.

1. Get a cellular phone or CB radio and keep it in your car. This is the quickest and safest way to alert the police or an emergency service when you need help.
2. Make or buy an automobile emergency kit.
3. Include a working flashlight, jumper cables, a warm blanket, and a well-stocked first-aid kit.
4. Carry a spare tire in good condition as well as the tools

necessary to change a tire. If you don't know how to change a tire, learn. It's not difficult, and it could save your life.

5. Carry a "Send Help" or "Please Call Police" sign to put in your windshield if your car is disabled on a busy highway.

6. Carry emergency flashers, flares, and an extra gallon of gas in a container made for gasoline.

7. When you get out of your car at a service station, even if only to pump gas, lock your car and take your keys with you. Leaving the door unlocked and the keys in the ignition invites a carjacking.

8. Put legal window tint on the driver's and passenger's windows. Put darker tint on the rear and back seat windows. This makes it difficult for thieves and harassers to do their job.

Practice safe parking habits

How many times have you heard or read that someone was attacked while walking to his or her parked car? Parking structures and parking lots are prime stalking areas because they are often dark, isolated, and lonely.

Each time you approach your vehicle, take a moment to make sure that you are safe from any assault. *Always:*

1. Take note of where you park—the row and column of a lot, the floor and section of a parking garage. Remember: if you look as if you don't know where you're going, assailants will find you an easy mark.

2. Lock your car and take the keys.

3. Put an "out of gas ... be back soon" note on the windshield.

4. As you return to your car, scan the parking area and the area around your car. Be alert for any suspicious activity, and be prepared to leave quickly if something doesn't look right. Be aware of vans. Abductors and rapists open up the side doors and pull in their victims every day.

5. Just before getting into your car, always check the back seat to

see if someone has entered the car while you were away. If you have a van or truck, carefully check ALL possible hiding places.

6. Look for signs of sabotage, such as large pools of fluid beneath the car, a flat tire, a smashed window. If you see something suspicious, immediately get to a safe place and ask for assistance or call a service station.

7. If you turn on the ignition and the radio begins to blare or the air conditioner and wipers go on, beware! An attacker may be planning to rob you while you are distracted.

8. Get in the habit of locking your car doors when you buckle your seat belt.

9. Remove valuables from your car that could be stolen by a valet. Too many valets steal. Don't give them the opportunity.

Change your behavior on the road

When driving, you generally feel safe from assault on the road. You are more likely to be thinking about avoiding accidents. But you should also be aware of certain danger points.

1. Never pick up hitchhikers. All too often, a harmless-looking young man or woman wants much more from you than a ride.

2. If you are being followed, do NOT go home. Instead, drive to a safe place such as a well-lit gas station, a busy store, or a police or fire station. As you drive, continuously honk your horn to attract attention.

3. Keep at least one car length between your car and the car in front of you for every 10 miles per hour of speed. Be sure you have enough room to drive around and out of a dangerous situation.

4. Be prepared to drive offensively if necessary. This means driving over curbs or on lawns and cutting across expressway lanes to exit quickly. In a dangerous situation, taking charge is safer than being timid.

5. If a person in another car waves a gun or shoots at you, duck, brake hard, and get behind that person's car. Then turn off the road as soon as possible and drive quickly to a safe place.

6. Do not engage in hand gestures with rude drivers. Such behavior may provoke a dangerous situation. (Some day I'll tell you about the time my uncle's friend Guido was given "the finger" while driving.)

7. If someone pulls up beside you to indicate there's something wrong with your vehicle, go to the nearest service station. In this way you can avoid a common ruse used by abductors.

Know how to handle emergency and police stops

If your car breaks down on the road, don't panic. Stay with your vehicle and wait for help. Unless you are traveling in a remote area, help is often only a few minutes away.

Try to get your vehicle to a safe place, out of traffic. Use your emergency flashers, or hang a white cloth from the antenna or door handle. Then stay inside the car and lock the doors.

When someone approaches your car to offer help, stay in the car. Crack the window just enough to communicate your situation. Ask the person to call for a tow truck or the police at the nearest telephone. NEVER get in a stranger's car for any reason. On major roads, law enforcement officers patrol regularly. All you have to do is wait.

Here are more tips if you have to stop on the road.

1. If you have a flat tire and haven't learned to fix it quickly or inflate it temporarily, it's better to drive on the flat to a service station than to put yourself in a dangerous situation.

2. In the event of a minor accident, stop only in a well-lit area. Carjackers often provoke such "accidents" just to get a victim to stop. Do NOT stop on a deserted, dark street. If necessary, drive to a well-lit area.

3. To exchange information with another driver after an accident,

roll your window down no more than two inches. Write your driver's license number and insurance information on a piece of paper and slip it through the window. Write down the other car's license plate number and description for your own records.

4. If you suspect a problem, immediately drive to a safe, well-populated area, not simply a well-lit one, and exchange information there. The law doesn't require you to exchange papers with violent people.

5. If you are stopped by the police, be sure the officer is indeed an officer. A legitimate police car should display red and blue lights on top or in the grill or dashboard. Officers should be in full uniform.

6. If you are stopped by an unmarked car and you doubt its legitimacy, ask the officer to call a marked car to the scene for verification. If the officer refuses, say something like:

> "I don't believe you are the police but I'll cooperate if you'll follow my car to a well-lighted place with lots of people around."

Then leave, driving slowly. If the officer is legitimate, the worst that can happen is that you'll have to explain your actions to a judge later. That's better than complying with a criminal's demands. Fake badges and uniforms can be purchased at K-Mart.

One time when I was at a car wash vacuuming my truck, I noticed a man paying particular attention to me. He stood about 5'8" tall, was balding, and had a beer belly. He wore grey slacks with a white-collared shirt and a tie. He was washing a late model Ford Crown Victoria.

Figuring he was some wacko, I just gave him an assertive look, finished up, and went on my way. About a mile down the road, beer belly pulled up beside me and yelled, "Pull over!"

My initial reaction was to stay calm and analyze the situation to figure out how I had attracted Roundboy into my life. He pulled over ahead of me and waved me to park in front of him. At this point I was ready to dial *SP (for the State Police) on my cell phone when those all-too-familiar blue lights started dancing in his front grill. So for laughs, I pulled over.

Keeping one foot on the gas and one foot on the brake, I screamed out the window, "Don't come near me! You don't look like a cop, so don't come near my truck! I will cooperate only if you get a marked vehicle to the scene, otherwise I'm outta here!"

He stopped in his tracks and said in a loud voice, "Are you Siciliano?"

"Who's asking?"

"I'm head of the state police in Peabody. I found your wallet at the car wash! You can come to the station and get it! Make sure you have proper ID."

Hey, what would you have done?

Avoid carjacking and kidnapping

Like most people, you probably don't worry too much about being kidnapped or having your car hijacked. But occasionally the newspapers carry a story about a carjacking by a desperate criminal trying to escape from police. More rarely you might read about someone being kidnapped and held for ransom.

Seldom will you read about a more frequent situation, probably because it is so common it is scarcely news: a man or a woman meets someone in a bar or at a party, accepts a ride, and is taken to an isolated area and assaulted. If you are concerned about kidnapping or carjacking, don't offer rides to or accept them from strangers. Vary your route to work, and avoid following a routine. Carjackers go for people who seem to be driving unconsciously.

If you are being kidnapped while you are in the driver's seat, make sure your seat belt is buckled and then suddenly ram a parked car or even a building to attract attention. Then get out and run to safety. If you are at an intersection, you can run red lights or rear-end the car in front of you, then get out and run.

As long as you survive, you
have done the right thing.

Don't be afraid to cause an accident. The consequences at the end of your journey with this individual could be worse than getting a little banged up while escaping.

Here are additional tips for getting away from an abductor.

1. While the kidnapper's attention is on the road, jump out—provided the car is moving slowly.

2. If you are in the passenger seat, put on your seat belt, grab the steering wheel, and yank it so that you crash the car into another car or a building.

3. Create a distraction by throwing a lit cigarette or lighted matchbook into your kidnapper's lap. When he stops get out and run.

4. Lock your car when getting gas. A car jacker can hide in your car when you go inside the station. It's happened.

Know what to do on long-distance drives

As with safety on the streets, many of the points in this section are self-evident. But have you never run out of gas on the road? How many times have you forgotten where you parked your car? When was the last time you decided not to lock it because you'd be gone for "only a few seconds"?

Driving for long distances poses its own set of safety risks. In addition to observing all the points in this chapter about general vehicle safety, consider several other factors when you do any long-distance driving.

1. Give friends or family an itinerary of your trip, including the

telephone numbers of hotels or motels where you will be making overnight stays. Check in with your family regularly.

2. Plan your road trips carefully. Be sure that your vehicle is in good condition, especially if you'll be driving in rough weather or terrain.

3. Carry good maps and familiarize yourself with the route you will travel before you leave.

4. Carry only enough cash to cover incidental expenses. Use credit cards or travelers checks to pay for food, lodging, gasoline, and so on.

5. Avoid deserted rest stops. Use service station or restaurant restrooms instead.

6. Always lock the doors when you leave your vehicle. Out-of-state license plates are an invitation to thieves.

7. Don't try to drive all night. Take frequent rests in well-lit, populated areas. Sleepy drivers are a hazard to themselves and everyone else on the road.

8. Contemplate using a mannequin as a "passenger" so it doesn't look as if you are driving alone.

Memorize all the safety tips so you will be prepared to use as many of them as you can the next time you drive.

3. Home safe home

Regardless of where you live, you'll want to make sure your home is a safe place to be when you're there and a secure place when you're not. The best way to accomplish this is to know how a burglar thinks. Remember, the burglar—like all criminals—is looking for an easy mark.

Often, thieves rob the same house two or more times because they know that insurance has replaced what they stole the first time.

If you suspect a burglary, do NOT enter your residence. Instead, go to a safe place and call the police.

If you startle a burglar in your home, escape immediately. If you cannot escape, be aware of the things in your home that you could use as a weapon. A broom, tools, a lamp, fireplace tools, articles of clothing, cleaning liquids, a rolled-up magazine (the blunt end used for jabbing), exercise gear, pots and pans—all can be used as weapons in an emergency.

Be creative. Improvise.

Here are more pointers that can help you prevent a burglary:

1. Install a home security system. A security alarm can be a very effective deterrent to criminal intruders. A variety of systems are available, ranging from inexpensive, battery-operated models to monitored motion-detection systems costing several thousand dollars. Post signs on your doors and fences indicating that your property is protected with an alarm system.

2. If you think an alarm system is too expensive, consider the cost of being robbed, or worse. Only 3 percent of American households have alarms. Statistics say that 97 percent of all home alarms are installed *after* a burglary. (I installed my alarm after I was burglarized. Hey, I learned my lesson so I could teach you *not* to learn the hard way.)

3. Do not put your name on your mailbox, which makes it too easy for a burglar to telephone to learn when the house is unoccupied.

4. Install a wide-angle peep hole in your doors. This is an inexpensive way to identify people at your doorstep. It also allows you to check the area before you leave your home or apartment to see if anyone is lurking nearby.

5. Never, under any circumstances, allow children to open the door.

6. Keep your house or apartment well lit.

7. Use motion-sensitive night lights on the outside of your house, and connect interior lights to timers that are set to turn on before evening. Leave some lights on all night.

8. You want to create the illusion that your home is occupied at all times.

If you're worrying about the electric bill, don't. A light bulb left burning for one month costs you a few dollars. That's peanuts compared to the risk to your safety if you turn it off.

---

9. Notify the city if street lights don't work. Burglars like the dark.

10. Do not leave windows open or uncovered. This allows casual observers to look directly into your home. During the day, draw the drapes or position the blinds to allow only enough light for plants. At night, cover your windows completely.

11. Keep the trees and shrubbery around your home well-trimmed. Overgrown bushes and trees often provide excellent hiding places for criminals.

12. Plant "defensive" shrubbery around your home, especially beneath windows. Bushes that have thorns or stiff, spiky leaves deter criminals.

13. Get a good watchdog. Barking dogs are the best burglar deterrents. The dog need not be large. Many small breeds have highly developed territorial instincts and make excellent watch-dogs.

14. Use broom handles or wooden dowels to secure sliding doors. Slide the dowel between the top of the sliding door and the frame. This will prevent it from being lifted out of the track.

15. Put nails in window frames so that windows can be opened only enough for ventilation. Not only does this simple technique prevent burglars from climbing in through the windows, but it also prevents small children from falling out.

**Keep some windows accessible for your
family's use in case of fire or other
emergency. Be sure your family knows
which windows are best for emergency exit.**

---

16. If your home is undergoing major construction or renovation and security is impaired, hire a guard, at least for nighttime.

17. Consider a second line or a cell phone in your bedroom. That's because burglars often remove a telephone from the receiver when they enter a home. Of course, an alarm system activated while you are sleeping will prevent a burglar from getting this far. Newer alarm systems also have cellular options, a safeguard even if the phone lines are cut.

18. If you live in a high crime area where law enforcement takes a while to respond, and if someone is trying to break into your home *while you are in it,* calling the fire department and reporting a fire will sometimes get help to the scene quicker. This is illegal, however, so do it only when you are desperate.

Strangers—a.k.a. home invaders

Often, homes are burglarized and their occupants terrorized by strangers posing as legitimate delivery people, utility meter checkers, and so on. When I appeared on the Montel Williams Show, it was as the expert on home invasion. The producers dressed me in a work uniform and made a fake badge for me. They wired me with a microphone and camera. I knocked on doors in a New Jersey middle class neighborhood trying to get into people's homes. My spiel was, "There has been a break in the sewer lines and it's mixed with public water. I need to check the colorization and pH of your water." Every house I went to, I was invited in. People are too trusting. Don't be fooled.

To reduce your chances of being victimized, keep the following points in mind.

1. Never open your door to a stranger. Criminals can get a good look at you and your home by posing as door-to-door sales-people, pizza or floral delivery people at the wrong address, or "neighbors" who have lost a pet. Don't underestimate these scumbags.

2. Never tell strangers you are home alone. If you are a woman and they ask for the man of the house, say he is napping and cannot be disturbed. Teach your children to say the same thing.

3. Do not broadcast your plans to be away from home in public places where others can overhear. Burglars and rapists can use the information to determine whether your home might be an easy target.

4. If a stranger comes to your door and asks to use your telephone to report an accident, tell him to wait outside while you call 911.

5. Ask someone you know to be present when service people are in your home.

6. Criminals sometimes pose as utility service people and ask to be let inside to read your meter. Virtually all service people carry picture IDs with the company name clearly visible. Ask to see the ID before you open the door. If you are in doubt, ask the person to wait outside while you call the company to verify his legitimacy.

7. Check the references, reputations, and backgrounds of people who apply to you for a job as housekeeper, babysitter, etc. If you have any doubts, don't hire them. I know of someone who worked for several home health care companies, constantly getting fired by one and hired by another. In the five years he worked in that role, he stole from every elderly client he had.

8. When long-term domestic employees leave, check your inventory and change your locks. Then send a nice thank you letter.

9. Do not leave jewelry, money, purses, or keys in sight when service people are inside your home. Take a minute for safety.

Keys and locks

Would you ever leave your door unlocked when you are away from home? Many people do because they feel they live in a safe neighborhood. But even "safe" neighborhoods are not really safe.

1. Keep your doors locked.
2. When you move into a new house or apartment, always change the locks. Have them rekeyed or have the tumblers reset. Otherwise, the previous residents, as well as any others to whom they might have given a key, have unrestricted access to your home.
3. Never hide an extra key under a mat, in a flower pot, or in any other easily accessible place. Criminals know all the hiding places. If you must hide a key somewhere, put it in an especially unusual location. (When you are at home, keep your own set of keys in a handy place in case of a fire or emergency.)

Locking doors is not paranoia; it's taking a minute for safety.

---

4. Lock your doors whenever you work in your yard, attic, laundry room, basement, or any other place where you can't see your home's entrances. While you're busy, burglars could easily enter your home unnoticed.
5. Do not count on an automatic garage door closer to securely lock your garage. If a burglar gets into a garage attached to your house, he can shut the door and leisurely pick the lock to the door into your home.
6. When you return home don't fumble with your keys at the door.

Make certain you have the key in your hand at the time you get off the bus or out of your car.

7. Multiple locks are more secure than single locks. One lock in each corner of the door is most secure. Use locks that require keys inside and outside on glass doors or doors with windows. Doors that must be opened with a key from the inside as well as the outside are a deterrent to a burglar attempting to remove large items, such as TV sets.

8. If you lose your keys and think they could be found by a criminal, change your locks.

Ask a locksmith or the police to inspect your residence and recommend the best locks for your situation. Take a minute for safety.

Storing valuables

1. Store valuables in a built-in safe or safety deposit box. If a fire occurs, your valuable papers, jewelry, pictures, and sentimental items will be secure.

2. Keep an inventory of all your valuables and write down how many spare keys you have and to whom you've given them. Keep these inventories and lists of keys in a safe place. Lock them in a safety deposit box at your bank or in a built-in safe in your home. Unless it is built-in, a home safe can itself be easily stolen. You do have a safe, don't you? Think safe.

3. Make sure that valuables cannot be easily seen from outside your home. Television sets, VCRs, stereo equipment, silverware, and other valuable items can be very tempting when the only thing stopping a burglar is a glass window.

4. Videotape every room, drawer, and closet in your home for insurance purposes.

A final thought: People whose homes have been broken into often compare the feeling to one of being personally violated. Some of them never feel secure in their homes again.

Your home is your castle. It is the one place in all the world where you should be able to feel completely safe and secure. The advice in this chapter can help you make your home the haven it should be. P.S: Get an alarm!

4. Vacation and travel safety

Vacationers are near the top of the list of crime victims. During a vacation your guard is down, and pleasure and relaxation are your primary focus. That makes you vulnerable to thieves and assailants. But if you visualize the things that could go wrong and prepare for them, you can have a safe and enjoyable vacation.

Business travelers are in a unique situation. The traveling executive often finds himself or herself in places domestic and international, without a clue as to what the new surroundings have in store. Different cultures can bring on a whole new set of rules.

Maintain your awareness of your surroundings. Any time, anywhere, *don't* let your guard down.

A friend of mine traveling in Mexico let a cute eight-year-old girl help him carry his bags at the airport. As you might guess, she ran off with a $3,000 laptop computer. He is now reading this book.

Remember, criminals don't take vacations, so be alert and be aware.

Securing your home while away

Whether you are planning to be gone for only a few days or for months at a time, you must secure your home before you leave. Many homes are broken into and vandalized while the owners are out of town because it is clear to anyone who is watching that nobody is at home.

Here are four important points to remember.

1. Tell only those who absolutely need to know that you'll be away. The fewer people who know about your trip, the safer your home will be.

2. Arrange for a neighbor or trusted friend to keep an eye on your home, to gather mail, newspapers, and the occasional flyer stuck in your door or your mailbox, to mow the lawn or shovel the snow, and to park a car in your driveway. You want your house to have that "lived-in" look. Don't stop deliveries of mail and newspapers, because your name and address ends up on a "stop list," which can become a resource for burglars.

3. If you have an answering machine, don't change your outgoing message to "Gone on vacation. See you in two weeks." Keep your old message and call into your machine every few days to clear your tape. Naturally, you won't want to invite burglars by posting a vacation message on your front door!

4. Don't tempt thieves by visibly packing your car the night before you leave. This shows that you'll be gone from home for a while.

Learn the culture

As for your safety while you are away from home, you've heard the old saying, "When in Rome. . . ." It's true. Looking and acting like a tourist is an excellent way to attract thieves. On the other hand, if you blend in with the local people, thieves won't notice you.

How do you do that? Here are some tips.

1. Familiarize yourself with strange cities, countries, and cultures before you leave home. At your local library, bookstores, and travel agencies are dozens of books, pamphlets, travel guides, maps, language guides, and other information on any area of the world. Encyclopedias and the American Automobile Association are also excellent sources of information.

2. Memorize key locations in the area you're visiting. And write

down the addresses and telephone numbers of places to contact for help if you need it—embassies, police stations, hospitals, airports, train stations, and so on.

3. Ask your hotel concierge or the local police which areas of the city should be avoided, particularly after dark.

4. Dress like the local people. Don't advertise the fact that you're a tourist by dressing in expensive vacation gear if everyone else is wearing jeans and T-shirts.

5. Check local laws about carrying Mace® or other defense weapons. These, by the way, cannot be carried onto a plane, although some airlines allow you to include them in check-on baggage.

6. Contact the U.S. State Department to learn about the political climate of your travel destination. Are the citizens hostile to Americans? Are there ongoing political or economic tensions that could erupt into overt hostility while you're in the country?

7. Don't offend the locals because of ignorance of their customs. You will not only be thought ill-mannered, but you will also be spotted by thieves in a minute. Before you arrive, learn enough of the language to communicate essential ideas. And learn the basic manners and customs of the area so you don't run the risk of being impolite.

8. Be able to recognize the uniforms of the police in the cities you will visit.

9. Be wary of offers of friendship or excessive attention from strangers, guides, and others you meet. All too often, tourists are lured into strange settings and then robbed.

General travel tips

1. Carry travelers checks and credit cards, not cash. If you must have cash, carry as little as possible.

2. Place valuables, one extra credit card, emergency cash, and emergency telephone numbers in a hotel safe.
3. Don't make a display of material wealth or be a heavy tipper.
4. Make two photocopies of the first two pages of your passport. Put one set in the hotel safe and one set in your luggage. This makes it easier to replace your passport if it is lost.
5. Don't wear clothing or items that obviously identify you as an American.
6. Don't wear or display items that identify your company. These are marks for terrorists and kidnappers.
7. Bring bottled water with you when you travel abroad. Americans take good water for granted, but many countries have poor or non-existent water purification facilities, and you can very easily become ill.
8. Avoid overindulging in alcohol or anything else that impairs your judgment.

I could write a hundred more examples of scams pulled on unaware Americans who've had their pockets picked and gotten scammed overseas. Consider this—there are professionals who will undoubtedly attempt to scam you. They have the ability to take a wallet out of a front pocket or a pocket book off the front seat of a car you are driving. They have been doing it for hundreds of years. Beware.

Perhaps the most important point of travel safety is this one: If a thief wants your money, your watch, your camera, or anything else of yours, give it to him! Don't risk getting hurt or killed. The following bears repeating:

**As long as you survive,
you've done the right thing.**

---

5. Safety in hotels

While the streets of a strange city may be dangerous, hotels can be even more so, perhaps because they feel like places of relative safety to a tired traveler. But there are many, many ways you can be robbed or assaulted while on a trip. Memorize the points listed below. They could save your life.

1. Choose a reputable hotel, preferably American, located in an area where crime is low.

2. Reserve a room on the second floor or higher, preferably in the middle of the corridor, not too far from the elevator or staircase.

3. Take a room facing the street or overlooking a swimming pool or other activities area. The likelihood of being easily spotted may deter someone from climbing in through your window.

4. When you are reserving a room, if the desk clerk blurts out your room number so others can hear, quietly request a new room.

5. Have a bellhop take your bags to the room. In this way you can ask the bellhop to inspect the room before you enter, check under the beds, in the closets, in the shower, behind curtains, and anywhere else someone might be hiding. Check immediately to be sure that all the locks are working properly.

6. If there is no bellhop, ask the manager to accompany you to your room. If this isn't possible, tell the desk to investigate immediately if you don't call within five minutes.

7. Whenever you enter your room, secure the deadbolt and chain locks. Make sure the peep hole works, and before unlocking your door use it to verify the identity of maids, room service attendants, or anyone else who knocks.

8. Portable travel locks, motion alarms, door braces, door jammers, and rubber wedges are available. Buy them and use them. They cost less than $25, and they ensure your safety when you're asleep.

9. Keep windows and balcony doors locked.

10. Be aware of suspicious people in the elevators and hallways.

11. Leave nothing of any value in your hotel room while you are gone. If you think for one second that your laptop computer, the information on your laptop, your jewelry, money, or anything else that has significant value to you is safe unattended in a hotel room, you might be delusional.

    Think about it: the person who makes your bed and cleans your room isn't paid much more than minimum wage. How tempting do you think it has to be to get them to steal an item from you that equals two weeks' pay to them?

    Think, too, how easy it is for a man in a three-piece suit to walk into your room while it is being cleaned, to say to the maid, "Excuse me, I just have to get something," and to grab a suitcase with all your camera equipment. They call that man a Con Artist.

12. When you leave the hotel for any reason, give your key to the front desk attendant. Doing so eliminates any possibility of losing your key, which may be stamped with the name of the hotel and your room number.

13. In case of fire, preplan an escape route by memorizing the location of your room in relation to stairways. Don't use the elevators. They can malfunction in heat and trap you.

14. Keep valuables and warm clothing at your bedside in the event of a hotel fire. Better yet, keep valuables in a hotel or room safe. Hotel fires occur with greater frequency than many people realize, and in other countries the building codes and fire regulations may be far less stringent than in the United States.

15. Be suspicious of a call from the front desk just after checking in requesting verification of your credit card number "because the imprint was unreadable." A thief may have watched you enter the motel room and called from the guest phone in the lobby.

6. Safety in airports

Airports are another haven for criminals. In the parking lot lurks the car thief and the mugger. Throughout the terminal are the scam artists and the pickpockets—and I don't mean the high-priced vendors. In the baggage claim area are the baggage thieves. Unfortunately, more and more reports are coming in that the baggage handlers themselves are actually slicing open your luggage with razor blades and removing your valuables.

Follow FAA guidelines. Dos and don'ts for safety and security have been implemented and revised since the 9-11 tragedy. What a passenger can and cannot take on a plane is listed on www.FAA.gov and no exceptions are made. There is no flexibility in these rules. Pay close attention to flight attendant instructions when aboard an aircraft.

Use the following tips to reduce your chances of becoming victimized:

1. During security screening be alert to anyone around you who is nervous, perspiring, impatient, or argumentative. With the new FAA orders in place, it's common knowledge that screening will take a while. The 9-11 tragedy was a humbling event that has made all passengers much more accommodating to security personnel and their screening methods. So anyone not complying with the new rules to any degree should raise a red flag.

2. If you must check your luggage, wait to see it go into the "chute" after it is taken from you. When booking your reservation, get a seat at the front of the plane so you can get to baggage claim quickly. That's because luggage is either carried on, lost, or stolen, or—if you are lucky—waiting at baggage claim.

3. Store your carry-on luggage across the aisle instead of over your head. You want to keep an eye on it. Otherwise someone can easily go into the overhead bin and remove your belong-

ings. Never put a pocketbook under the seat. The person behind you can remove a credit card and you might not know it for a couple of days.

4. When riding in a shuttle bus, don't let your luggage leave your side no matter what. The rear compartment can be opened while the bus is stopped at a traffic light. People are constantly getting on and off the bus at different stops just to steal luggage.

5. Because tags fall off or get ripped off, put photocopies of your passport, ID, and itinerary in your luggage. In case a bag gets lost, someone who recovers it will be able to forward it to you.

6. Place any baggage, laptops, or briefcases on the counter in front of you when you stand at rental car, hotel, and airport ticket counters. If you put these at your feet to the left, right, or behind you, you become a prime target for distraction thieves. For example: a very emotional person walks up to you while you are waiting for the clerk at the counter, asks you how to get to the Alamo, and then starts to cry. In the confusion, an accomplice sneaks up behind you and removes the laptop that you placed on the floor next to you.

7. Don't take your eyes off your belongings while they are going through security or screening checkpoints. This is a prime location for distraction thieves to steal laptops, pocketbooks, and briefcases. Once you put your belongings on the movable belt, one thief distracts you from immediately going through the metal detector by either dropping a handful of change, causing a scene, clipping a metal object to the back of your coat that will cause a delay, or saying, "Hey, don't I know you?"— anything to keep you from going through the metal detector for 30 seconds while the accomplice walks through clean and picks up your belongings. If you become distracted for an instant your valuables are gone! With security as tight as it is, this crime is harder to commit but still being done.

8. Never leave your bags unattended. They can be stolen. It happens every day. Rarely, but worse, someone looking for the opportunity could hide bombs or drugs in your bags. Terrorists can conceal plastic explosives or other lethal weapons in articles that someone would ordinarily purchase at the terminal newsstand, such as a book, soda can, candy bar, or magazine. Such devices can be wired with components from cell phones or beepers, and when called from the ground moments after takeoff can trigger an explosion.

9. Do not overstuff your luggage. It can pop open easily. In addition, stuffed luggage looks to a thief as if there might be something of value in it.

10. Don't use fancy, expensive luggage. It's a red flag to a thief.

11. Put all electronics, cash, jewelry, medicine, and important papers in your carry-on luggage.

12. Ignore other people arguing and strangers who are overly friendly. These could be staged distractions to make it easier for a thief or pickpocket to rob you.

13. Be alert to anyone in the baggage claim area paying undue attention to you.

14. Don't let anyone help you with your airport locker (if you can even find one nowadays). Someone might insert quarters for you to appear helpful but then give you a different key without your knowledge.

15. Be aware of any contact with others, even if it is a good deed they are doing. They could be setting you up.

16. Request a seat next to the plane's emergency exit. Each time you get on a plane review the instructions for opening the door. However, anyone who does not feel he or she could prevent a disgruntled passenger from opening an emergency exit during flight should not sit in these rows.

17. Request window seats in a plane's coach section. Hijackers

often take hostages from first-class aisle seats.

18. If your plane is hijacked, do NOT make eye contact with the hijackers, which can increase the chances that you will be singled out for attention. Stay calm, follow directions, don't argue, and don't attempt heroics—at least not yet. These are desperate people.

19. Don't tell a stranger your plans. The accomplices of hijackers often disguise themselves as passengers.

20. We have all learned by example that coming together as a physical force we can overpower hijackers or air-ragers. Any-one becoming aware of a potential threat has a responsibility to make others aware of the situation. First steps include making the crew aware, one on one. However, depending on the volatility of the situation, it could be necessary to quickly bring attention to the cause by rallying passengers first. Use caution to avoid unnecessarily alarming others or escalating what could be a volatile situation.

21. Be aware of potential weapons that can still be smuggled onto an airplane: explosives, pepper spray, razor blades, knives, and even guns made of metal or plastic. Undetectable by a metal detector, plastic, wood, and glass can all be shaped into sharp, lethal devices. In addition, plenty of items that belong on an airplane could be used as weapons, including hot water or coffee, serving carts, bags, blankets, headset cords, shoes, pens, batteries, and keys. Even the blunt end of a rolled-up magazine can be used to jab.

22. In foreign countries, arrive at the airport as close to departure time as possible and wait in an area away from crowds. If a bomb has been planted, it is more likely to go off in high-traffic areas.

23. When renting a car in a foreign country, rent one that is common in that country. Make sure that any rental car in

America or abroad doesn't have "rental" written all over it. Don't ride in fancy cars or limos, as they only bring more attention to you. Follow rules for car safety that begin on page 19.

24. Guard your passport and tickets carefully. There are many undesirables looking for a new identity who would love to have your passport.

Memorize these travel tips and follow them carefully. If you are aware of what could happen, you can guard against it.

7. Safety when using public transit

Every day, newspaper headlines report another assault on a subway, bus, or commuter train. Here's how to protect yourself against the chance that it could happen to you.

1. When you are riding the bus, subway, or train, know which are the best lit and most populated stops. Avoid exiting in an area that is unfamiliar to you.

2. Wait at a train stop with a group. If there are few or no other people at the stop, stand near the ticket booth.

3. On a bus sit close to the driver. Be alert to any new passengers or unusual behavior.

4. If another passenger appears suspicious, move immediately to a seat farther away. Stay alert.

The key is to be aware.

---

5. If a suspicious person exits behind you, immediately get back on the bus. Continue to the next stop before exiting.

6. Vary the route you travel each day and don't let your guard down—whether in familiar territory or not.

7. Don't encumber yourself with luggage or packages. Keep your hands free.

8. If you are in a crowd and feel hands on your wallet or purse, create a scene. Very loudly, say, "Whoever has their hands on me had better take them off NOW!

Don't think that nothing could ever happen to you. But don't be paranoid either. Do watch for potential problems. Do keep an eye on other passengers. Remember the tips about walking alone given at the beginning of this chapter. Many apply to public transit: Know where you are going; stay in well-lit and populated areas if possible; and, above all, carry yourself with an attitude of confidence and strength.

We are all too aware that terrorists are targeting areas where large numbers of people congregate, including public transportation facilities. Although the chances are slight that you'd encounter an attacker loaded with explosives, you do have a chance of disabling the person. Upcoming chapters tell you of self-defense and restraint techniques that can put an attacker at a disadvantage. Doing nothing and simply allowing the attacker to follow through is a death sentence.

Public transportation need not be dangerous if you know what to do in a questionable situation.

8. Safety on the telephone

The telephone is indispensable in today's world. With new technology constantly being developed, Alexander Graham Bell's little talking machine is becoming more versatile than ever. But each new technological improvement also creates an opportunity for thieves, stalkers, and other kinds of criminals.

Bugs, taps, and snoops are all devices meant to spy on your conversation. If you have something important to say or an important document to fax, and if you don't want your competition to get its sticky little hands on it, you must take appropriate steps. A number of agencies and devices can be used to combat espionage.

For more information, call me at 800-2-GET SAFE.

Another terrible problem in this country involves a type of boiler room operation called a phone scam. Eighty percent of these crimes are targeted to the elderly. Most of the time the scam artists say, "You have won 50,000 dollars!" They pump you up, get you all emotional, then tell you that in order to collect your money you have to send $2,000 to insure the shipment.

About 1,200 of these operations exist, and they make a lot of money. They sell their call lists to each other, so it is not uncommon for them to hit the same person four to five times. They even call back posing as lawyers who offer to get your money back for you —if you send them a fee.

How do you protect yourself and your privacy from these people? Here's how.

1. If you are a single woman living alone, don't publish your first name in the telephone book. Use an initial instead.

2. If you receive suspicious calls, hang up. If the annoyance continues, contact the police and the telephone company.

3. Don't give information to strangers on the telephone. Thieves often target homes by posing as pollsters, bankers, credit card companies, or police to gather information about whether you live alone or have a pet or an alarm system, how much money you make, when and where you work, how often you travel, and so on.

> **You have the right to refuse to give out information on the phone. Don't feel guilty about refusing.**

4. If you use an answering machine, do not announce your name and number as part of the message. Avoid giving criminals any information about yourself. A common mistake is revealing

your exact whereabouts in a message.

5. Consider keeping a separate line or a cellular phone beside your bed as a security device. A cellular phone is especially useful because there are no wires for thieves to cut.

6. Never give important information over a cellular telephone. For under $100, anyone can buy scanning equipment that enables them to listen in on your conversations. For example, let's say you call a rug company for an in-house estimate for wall-to-wall carpeting. The call is made on your cell phone and goes something like this:

   "Thank you for calling Acme Rug. How can I help you?"

   "I'm calling for an estimate."

   "Okay. Please give me your full name and address, and I will have a sales rep contact you for an appointment."

   Meanwhile a criminal is listening in on his scanner. A short time later, you, the unsuspecting consumer, receive a call from the impostor. You set up an appointment with a phony rug salesman who has found his next victim.

7. If you lose a pet, jewelry, your wallet, or other item, be suspicious of anyone who calls saying they found it and they want to meet you somewhere to return it. If this happens, call police and have them accompany you to the meeting place.

8. Most newer models of telephone have a small screen that automatically shows you the caller's telephone number while you are on the line. Ask your local phone company to describe caller ID and get the service if available in your area.

9. Besides caller ID, most telephone companies have a service that can automatically trace incoming calls. After the caller hangs up, you punch in a code which tells a computer to record the date, the time, and the caller's telephone number. Ask your local phone company if they have this service, and then use it for suspicious calls.

10. Teach children these tips on telephone security. Tell them to use the answering machine to screen calls when you are not home.

11. Protect your calling card number. When punching in that number, be wary of everyone in the area. Sometimes the guy standing at the phone next to you is talking to his accomplice and telling him your number. In an airport, thieves could be videotaping a "going away" couple right behind you as you punch in your digits. The best one is when a thief stands on the second level of an open area, such as in an airport, and watches you with binoculars. Fraudulent use of calling cards is beating out check fraud in the number of dollars lost.

The telephone is a remarkable instrument for bringing people together. But it also offers many ways for unscrupulous characters to violate your privacy—or your safety. Be aware. Don't be a victim.

9. Safe dating

People always ask me, "How did you get into personal security?" It was a result of being the target of the neighborhood bullies and being mugged when I was 12. Mugging is a significant emotional event at any age, and especially at 12.

In addition, I've always had a difficult time accepting one thing in particular. When I was 13, a young girl confided in me that she had been raped. I didn't really know what sex was, much less rape, but being the inquisitive little shaver I was, I found out quickly. I was devastated by the information. Trying to imagine the pain and the violation she must have felt overwhelmed me.

In the next couple of years I met five more young women who confided the same violation to me. By the age of 15 I knew half a dozen women who'd been raped. As you can imagine, this awareness at age 15 had a profound effect on the way I viewed the world.

Police and hospitals well know that there are many more rapes than are ever reported. This is especially true of "date rape," or assault of a woman by a man she knows. Date rape is growing more common on high school and college campuses. It often occurs in someone's home or dormitory or an automobile.

Many women and girls fear that reporting an attack will make the rapist angry and bring on more aggression. Some women are reluctant to humiliate a man they think is a "friend."

A large number of women and girls believe they themselves were somehow responsible for having provoked a sexual assault by having given off a signal they weren't aware of or by simply having agreed to go on a date with the person.

It is important to realize that even on a date, even with someone you think you know well, you must stay alert. Know that you have the right to say "No," no matter how much money a man might spend on the date.

While rape between strangers is condemned by society as a violent, criminal act, incidents of date rape are often minimized, largely due to our social training. Even today, girls are given the message from childhood on that they will be popular if they are submissive and compliant, while boys are taught that aggression and physical force are "manly."

Surveys show that some men and women still believe such myths. Some men believe that when a woman says "No" she really means "Yes," or that a man has a right to force sex on a woman if he has spent money on her or thinks she has "led him on."

Although a woman should never feel guilty or ashamed of being victimized, she may be able to reduce the likelihood of such an incident by taking certain precautions.

Know that you have the right to set sexual limits. You may have different limits with different people and your limits may change. But decide what you want or don't want before you end up in the back seat of a car. Then communicate those limits to your date.

Trust your feelings. If you FEEL you are being pressured into unwanted sex, you're right.

Pay attention to behavior that seems odd or pushy—such as when someone:

- sits or stands too close to you and enjoys your discomfort
- engages in power stares, looks through you or down at you
- blocks your way intentionally
- speaks or acts as if he knows you more intimately than he does
- grabs or pushes you
- doesn't listen to you or disregards what you are saying, especially if you are saying "No."

Be assertive. Get angry when someone does something to you that you don't want. Respond immediately, and communicate your exact desires clearly.

Stand up for yourself, even if it means being rude. It's perfectly okay to be rude to someone who is sexually pressuring you, even if his feelings get hurt. After all, he's not paying any attention to your feelings.

Here are some ways to reduce the likelihood of date rape.

1. When you date someone for the first time, meet during the day in a public place like a restaurant, a movie, or wherever there is a crowd. Do group activities like double dating or playing miniature golf. If the two of you are alone, have lunch, not dinner. That way, you'll build in a time limit.

2. Have your own transportation. Don't depend on your date to get you home. It's all too common for a woman to be driven to a secluded location and then assaulted. Also carry enough money for your own meals, tickets, and so on. Don't ever depend on anyone financially. Many men still believe that any

woman they spend money on owes them sexual favors.

3. Don't use drugs or alcohol. If you do drink, know your limits. When you drink, the first thing you lose is your judgment.

4. If you're at a party, never accept a ride from someone you've just met. Call a cab instead.

5. Watch out for men who become violent or won't take no for an answer, even in nonsexual situations.

6. It's a good idea to be clear with your date right from the start regarding your feelings about sex. Saying "No" is a lot easier at dinner than at your doorstep. Establish at the outset what your expectations are, what you will and won't allow, when you are uncomfortable, and that "No" means NO. If you feel uncomfortable with your date's responses or behaviors, clearly communicate those feelings.

Don't take communication for granted.

---

7. If you invite your date in for a nightcap or coffee and he becomes aggressive, don't hesitate to go to a friend's or neighbor's home to call the police.

8. Don't automatically trust everyone. Have a written set of guidelines for dealing with unwelcome sexual behavior that you can teach your children.

9. Evaluate your own self-esteem. If it's low, you might be attracting the wrong kinds of people. Low self-esteem leads many women to accept unacceptable behavior from a man. Some of the warning signs, which should NOT be ignored, include mood swings, fits of anger, inability to handle frustration, sexist jokes and behavior, overly controlling behavior, and lack of consideration for the feelings of you or others. Does your date insult you or demean you in front of friends? Does he

pressure you for sex? Abuse alcohol or drugs? If you are attracting or tolerating these kinds of people, seek counseling. Or take a self-defense course.

10. Take it slowly in the early stages of a relationship. Don't give out your address too soon. Get to know the person thoroughly. Cultivate your relationships as you would cultivate a plant. Let them grow at a natural pace.

11. Internet dating has become very popular. Most people listed on Internet dating sites are sincere about finding a partner. However, there are people—men and women both—you should be wary of. Don't give anyone online your real email address, last name, phone number, address, or place of work during your early correspondence. Stop communicating with anyone who tries to pressure you into giving this information.

12. Check with your ISP (Internet Service Provider) to make sure that your online profile does not give out more personal information than you are comfortable with.

13. Never give out any personal details until you are 100 percent certain that the person you are communicating with is for real. Do not communicate your address until you have met the person in a public place and feel comfortable. Ideally, without giving out your Social Security number, get the other person's and do a criminal background check.

14. Never arrange to meet anyone until you have exchanged telephone numbers, spoken to each other a few times, and developed a good gut feeling about them. Ensure that you swap landline numbers and not just cell/mobile phone numbers.

15. Never *ever* give out personal financial details! This includes details about wages, investments, and bank or credit cards. If someone is interested in the details of your finances, cease contact immediately; no explanations are necessary. Never send any money to anyone you've recently met on a dating site.

If you are asked for money, that person's intentions are not genuine. Cease contact immediately!

16. Drop correspondence with those who do not accept your feelings and who act in a controlling manner. Relationships are built on honesty, respect, and acceptance.

What to do if attacked

If your date starts to get out of hand, explain firmly that you want him to stop and insist that he respect your wishes. If this doesn't work:

1. Leave. Lie if necessary. Say that you have to go to the bathroom, and then take off.

2. Yell "NO! I told you to stop and I mean it. Now leave!" If that doesn't work, *you* leave—immediately. Go to the nearest place of safety: the neighbor's house, a gas station, a police station.

3. If he won't let you go, gouge his eyes out! (See chapter 4.) Fight as hard and as determinedly as you would if he were a stranger. By assaulting you, he has crossed the line, and now he *is* a stranger. Remember: You are worth fighting for!

4. If all else fails, you can always let him kiss you, then bite down on his lip until your teeth meet! Then, run, run, run!

10. Safety for children

Tragically, 50,000 children are reported missing every year. Additionally, one in four children falls victim to inappropriate touching. In 85 percent of the cases, the predator is known to the victim. Thinking "it won't happen to my kids" or "I'm pretty aware of what goes on" is exactly what a pedophile hopes you think. Children might be sleeping in their beds while you're in the basement, and someone walks right in and takes them. The fact is, you can't be everywhere at once.

Raising children successfully can be the greatest achievement of a parent's life. And one of the great pleasures of raising a family is teaching children to trust and love. Unfortunately, however, the world is a dangerous place.

Although you don't want to train your children to be paranoid or cynical, they have to learn to deal safely with strangers. Children are quick learners and will easily pick up the good habits that can protect them from assault or abuse. Here are some things to know.

1. Scare tactics don't work. You don't teach kids to swim by telling them how not to drown. Give children fundamental strategies that make them aware of life's hazards and how to effectively avoid and remove themselves from dangerous situations.

2. Raise responsibly. This means to teach them to be in control of their lives early on. They are ultimately responsible for their own safety. They can sense danger. By allowing them to grow on their own without smothering them, they can make more effective decisions.

3. Never too young to learn. Even three- to five-year-olds are able to make certain judgments, think for themselves, and recognize right from wrong. Making them aware of the following tips gives them tools they can use to identify predators.

4. Yes and No—During the terrible twos, yes and no are the two most common words. This is the age when small children are learning their likes and dislikes, so this is also a prime time to allow them to speak up and show them how to do so. Never oppress a child's need to communicate feelings.

5. Play games. Take your child on a journey of what if__? By playing "What If__?" you can get an idea of your children's thought processes and how they view the world. Start slowly with simple questions, like: "What if you couldn't find Mommy in the supermarket? What would you do?" Gradually work your way into "What if someone you know asked you to take

a walk and Mommy didn't know about it?" This line of questioning lets children think for themselves and allows you to feed them the appropriate responses. Just don't scare them.

6. Strangers—generalize; never color code. Most kids think a stranger is a tall guy in a black-hooded trench coat. When using examples of who, when, and where, be careful not to describe specific locations or times of day. This could make children afraid of the dark or feel overly safe during the day and let their guard down. Explain precautions using a variety of demographic examples and keep it light and interesting.

7. Teach your children their address and telephone number as soon as they can talk. Also teach them their parents' first and last names and work telephone numbers.

8. Teach your children to pretend they are not alone when someone calls your home. Have them tell callers who wish to speak to a parent that the parent is busy or taking a nap.

9. Tell your children not to talk to people who are doing telephone surveys. The caller could be someone trying to learn your schedule or the value of the contents of your home.

10. Tell your children to walk away from any car that stops near them. Tell them not to talk with any adult asking for directions. Role play a situation, showing children how to walk away and ignore a stranger who asks them a question.

Role playing helps counteract a child's natural tendency to be polite and obedient with adults.

---

11. Let a trusted neighbor know if your child will be home alone after school. Make certain that your child knows the neighbor's telephone number.

12. Tell your child to stay away from dark alleys or shortcuts. Kids

love the shortest way home because it makes them feel smart and independent. Tell them that smart kids take the well-traveled and well-lighted routes.

13. Make sure your child knows that hitchhiking is very dangerous!

14. Even young children have good instincts about what could be a dangerous situation. Reinforce those instincts. Tell them it's okay to say "No!" or to simply run away from someone they feel uncomfortable with. Societal influences start to suppress a child's instincts and to discount them at an early age. Allow instincts to flourish. Encourage children to pay attention to their inner voice. When children are allowed to speak up and encouraged to express their feelings, they are in a much stronger position.

15. Personalized clothing or bags can make it easy for a stranger to pretend he knows your child. Don't give him the chance. Kids in groups without distinctive clothes are always safer.

16. Many police departments are suggesting that parents teach children the "secret code" system. Decide on a word that your child will remember, maybe one he has thought of himself. Make that your secret password. Tell your child to never accept a ride from anyone who doesn't know the password, even if it is a person he or she knows. After the code word has been given to anyone outside your immediate family, change it.

**If you ask someone to pick up your child
from school or day care,
give this person the password.**

---

17. Teach children to never accept a ride from a stranger, and never to go with someone who wants them to help look for a lost pet or who offers them money, candy, or anything else.

18. Children should be taught to never go with someone who says, "We caught your friend stealing, and we'll arrest you if you don't come with us," or "Your mother has been hurt and we're here to take you to the hospital."

19. If someone is trying to take your child somewhere against her will, tell her to run or struggle as hard as she can. At the same time, she should yell, as loudly as she can:
    "THIS IS NOT MY MOMMY!" or
    "THIS IS NOT MY DADDY!"

20. If your child feels that she is in danger, tell her to run to a place where there are lots of other people.

21. Have your child take a self-defense course.

Children on the Internet

Let's not forget the dangers to children of the Internet. The fact is that your kids probably know as much if not more about computers than you do. The Internet is a public forum that anyone has access to from anywhere. Many undesirable people are online seeking out children.

Get to know your PC and what it is capable of.

Dozens of online sites exist to help you keep your kids safe. Research these sites by simply typing the words "children internet security" into a search engine. Dozens of options will present themselves for you to choose from.

Children in chatrooms pose the biggest risk. Do the research: "12yr-oldamy@anyemail.com" could very well be 40-year-old pedophile Ed. Study up on this. I could write another whole book on it.

Learn about and invest in software that has parental controls to filter out smut. I can't begin to tell you what exists online. Photos and videos on the Internet are available just a few clicks away that contain images I never thought were humanly possible. There are some things that people, not just kids, should never see. Without getting into detail, I can tell you that videos depicting actual rapes are becoming popular. And that's just the beginning.

When your kids go to play at a friend's house, discuss the subject of Internet security with their parents, especially if the friend has older siblings. Teens everywhere have undoubtedly acquired access to this stuff. If they are downloading music, they also have access to everything else.

In addition to teaching children about being safe around other people, teach them what to do in case of fire. Show them how to use a fire extinguisher and be sure that your home fire extinguishers are within the reach of your children. Identify the best escape routes with them and practice fire drills.

About sexual abuse of children

In recent years it has become clear that children are and have been the victims of sexual abuse much more often than anyone in the idyllic 1950s ever imagined. It is crucial to be very clear with a child about what is and what is not appropriate touching, because children can easily become confused, especially when, as is often the case, the abuser is a family friend or relative. Moreover, an abused child is too easily persuaded to hide the abuse.

1. Tell your children that although most people are good, some are not. Tell them they can and should come to you whenever something has happened to make them feel uncomfortable. Do not get angry with them when they do come to you, even if you think they have been careless. No matter what a child has done, it is never the child's fault if he or she has been victimized.

2. Teach children the difference between good and bad touching. Tell them that if someone touches them where their bathing suits are worn, they should run and yell as hard as they can.

3. Tell your children to report to you anyone who touches them indecently, even if the person tells them: "You'll get in trouble if you do," or "Let's keep this our secret," or "I'll hurt your

puppy (brother, sister, family) if you tell."

4. Pedophiles often try to keep their victims from revealing their behavior by saying it is a secret. Don't allow your children to keep secrets for any reason, and set a good example by not keeping secrets from them.

5. Reassure your children that if someone touches them "like this," it's not their fault. Tell them you love them and they are doing the right thing by telling you if something happens that they don't like, even if it means breaking a secret.

Keep an eye out for incest. Statistically, family members are responsible for up to 20 percent of cases of sexual abuse, with up to 5 percent of these cases involving a father and daughter. Stepfathers are more likely than biological fathers. A father also holds an influential position in a family and is trusted by the mother.

Children who are abused are highly likely to abuse other children. Among those who have access to children in isolated situations are entrusted friends, civic-oriented authority figures who coach sports, religious leaders, and camp counselors. Make sure your child's school is performing criminal background checks on all its employees and volunteers.

If, despite all efforts, your child is molested, get professional counseling. The child may act as if everything is all right, but unresolved anger and shame can surface years later, making it difficult or impossible for him or her to build good relationships as an adult.

"If my survival caused another to perish, then [my] death would be sweeter and more beloved."

—Kahlil Gibran, "The Voice of the Poet"

"I don't agree!"

—Robert L. Siciliano, the voice of a survivor

:01

Chapter 3
The 10 Laws of Survival

Attitude

The longer I live, the more I realize the impact of attitude on life.

Attitude, to me, is more important than facts.

It is more important than the past, than education, than money, than circumstances, than failures, than success, than what other people think or say or do.

It is more important than appearance, giftedness, or skill.

It will make or break a company, a church, a home.

The remarkable thing is we have a choice every day regarding the attitude we will embrace for that day.

We cannot change our past . . . we cannot change the fact that people will act in a certain way.

We cannot change the inevitable.

The only thing we can do is play on the one string we have, and that is our attitude . . .

I am convinced that life is 10% what happens to me and 90% how I react to it.

And so it is with you.

—Charles Swindoll

The 10 Laws of Survival

"Violence is as American as cherry pie."

—H. Rap Brown

Violence has always been and will always be part of human existence. Accept it. Decide now that you will not become a helpless victim. Know that you are responsible to yourself and your family to stop an assault, to stop a terrorist act or to prevent the overall destruction of humanity. You've got the power!

Any violence against you, your family, or your co-workers should be met with force. No one has the right to inflict harm on you or your children at any time for any reason. The mere thought of it should trigger offensive thoughts requiring a defensive response.

In the seminars I conduct, I ask: "How many of you know what you would do in response to an assault? How many of you would fight back?" The answer is always less than 10 percent. Then I ask, "To all of you who have children, how many of you would know what to do if you saw someone attacking your child?" Amazingly,

95 percent of the hands go up. Every time. People have a hard time thinking about protecting themselves, but they have no reservations about protecting their children. This disparity is called civilized conditioning.

The main obstacle you face is—well, you're too nice. You have been brought up in a culture that generally teaches people to be civil toward one another. We're taught to be kind and loving, caring and giving. We're told from the time we are little, be nice to your brother and don't hit your sister.

As we grow older we're taught manners: shake hands, give hugs and kisses, sit up straight, and keep your elbows off the table. Eventually we go through formal schooling, get careers, find a mate, have babies, and become productive, civilized Americans.

At no point does anyone sit us down and say, "Somebody, some day, might try to cause you a great deal of harm. Here is everything you need to know to prevent it." As a result, we are unprepared to confront violence.

This civilized conditioning, as wonderful as it is in helping us get along with others, suppresses our instinctual need for survival. Most of us when confronted in an attack situation freeze up and become overwhelmed with fear and panic.

Not everyone is as nice as you. Unfortunately, some people are taught, through no fault of their own, to be bullies. They become mean and nasty, the scum of the earth. These predators come in all shapes, sizes, colors, genders, religions, and professions. Do a search through your local police department of sexual predators registered in your town. You'll be astonished.

All is not lost. With a little reprogramming we can get you into a frame of mind for avoiding dangerous situations and removing yourself from them.

If you are serious about preparing for the eventuality of an

assault, I strongly suggest that in addition to studying the techniques in this book you take a self-defense course. Only by physically practicing the habits of self-defense, not simply reading about
them, will your instincts learn to reassert themselves.

The 10 Laws of Survival depend upon your cultivating your
natural instincts and effectively using the qualities of fear, anger,
aggressiveness, submissiveness, decisiveness, awareness, assertiveness, body language, voice, and eye contact.

Survival law 1: Use fear

"Let me assert my firm belief that the only thing that we have to fear is fear itself—nameless, unreasoning, unjustified terror which paralyzes needed efforts to convert retreat into advance."

—Franklin D. Roosevelt

Human beings are born with two fears: the fear of loud noises and the fear of falling. Every other fear is learned behavior.

Fear is the underlying motivator in much of daily life. Some fears are healthy, but others can be detrimental. An example of unhealthy fear is staying in a destructive personal relationship because you fear abandonment. Healthy fear, on the other hand, is staying far behind a reckless driver on the expressway so that you don't run the risk of an accident.

Fear is that gut feeling you get when you know something is wrong. Recognize that feeling, and use it whenever your safety might be at risk.

This fear is what motivates you to fight for your survival. Don't fight the fear. Let it enter your consciousness. Let yourself feel it. Once you recognize that you're afraid, you have already won half the battle.

Fear can help or hinder human performance. Fear is instrumental in helping you avert danger and can supply you with the strength to fight. Fear brings on adrenaline. When your heart starts racing and your body starts quivering that's adrenaline rushing through your body. Adrenaline is capable of providing you with great strength. However, if not channeled properly it can paralyze you.

When you panic, you stop breathing. Oxygen is restricted or cut off, making your muscles weak. Your blood rushes to your inner organs and away from your arms, legs, and head. At this point you freeze. You can't scream, dial a phone, or find your keys.

To stop the panic and get the blood circulating freely again, you must do two things.

1. You must yell a loud "NO!" This releases the panic and sends blood and oxygen to your head so you can think properly.
2. You must make two fists. Doing this will send the blood to the arms and legs so you can move.

One way to make this response automatic is to program your mind to associate fear with the word "No!"

Every time you are startled and you feel fear, think the word "No!"

An exercise that will reinforce this is to have a friend sneak up on you two or three times a month and try to scare you. Each time this happens, scream the word "No!"

Remember the old Pink Panther movies? Inspector Clouseau, to keep his defenses sharp, had his butler attack him every time he came home. You may not wish to go to such extremes, but I'm sure you could play with the concept.

Survival Law 2: Use anger

"Anger is like a fire extinguisher.
It is to be used only in case of emergency."

—Anonymous

On a beautiful New England Spring evening long ago, 50 to 60 of the locals, including me, got together to celebrate the end of a semester. The location was high on top of a woodsy hill adjacent to the town's golf course. We were all young and full of ego—and beer. I had been socializing with a small group of friends when suddenly everything turned black. I awoke on my back with a psychopath perched on top of me. He was using my head as a punching bag.

Apparently I had been grabbed from behind and put in a "sleeper hold" that rendered me unconscious. When I awoke I managed to startle the psycho enough to get him off me so I could remove myself from the attack and run to safety.

Two days later I found myself in the same room as this animal. He began to growl, like a dog whose territory is invaded. Then Psycho began to literally punch himself in the face, turn around, and charge toward me! He came full speed like a bull after a cape, swinging his fists violently. Without hesitation I gave him a strong upcut to his chin and sent him careening into a few chairs.

He was angry at the world. I used anger for my survival.

Anger is another emotion that can help or hinder human performance. Anger can make you act blindly and irrationally, or it can make you act with great power, concentration, and determination.

If you are assaulted, you naturally feel fear and anger. But you can channel the immense energy of these emotions into an explosive counterattack.

Fear and anger are similar in nature and can be used in tandem. In an attack situation, your life depends on your ability to respond with anger and concentrate on destroying your attacker. While we have a hard time thinking about our own self-preservation, we have thoughts of rage when considering someone attacking our child or spouse. Harness that anger and use it to your advantage.

As you learned from Survival Law 1 on using fear, the way to energize your anger is to immediately do something positive and assertive.

Shout "No!" in a loud, authoritative voice. This action not only comes as a surprise to your assailant, it also affects your own emotions. It triggers your anger and allows you to defend yourself swiftly, violently, and effectively.

That kind of focused anger and violent counterattack does not come easily to many people. In fact, it is not unusual for some people to believe that they are incapable of gouging someone's eyes or kicking his groin.

They may hesitate to inflict pain or injury. Or they may feel, consciously or unconsciously, that fighting back would be hopeless, that they would be defeated in the end and possibly seriously harmed. If this describes you, you must cultivate your anger through purposeful mental conditioning and by understanding that nobody has the right to threaten or attack you.

Survival Law 3: Use aggressiveness

"Remember, when things look bad and it looks like you're not gonna make it, then you gotta get mean. I mean plumb, mad dog mean! 'Cause if you lose your head and give up, then you neither live nor win. That's just the way it is."

—Josey Wales

It happened in a public place. With a friend, pizza was the agenda. A little extra parmegiano and a sprinkle of spicy pepper were the only heat that interested me. In walked Big Billy Bagadonuts—obviously raised with a silver shovel in his hand.

"Hey, Siciliano, how about you come over here and let me wipe the ground with your face!"

I responded, "Go eat a donut."

Big Billy charged me with intent to snap my little twig body in half when I remembered what good ole Dad used to say. "Rob, whenever someone bigger than you intends to hurt you, pick up something and whack 'em with it!"

Taking Dad's advice to heart, I grabbed a chair and whacked the bully on the right side of his body, stopping him instantly.

Improvised weaponry is to be used only in a potentially life-threatening situation. "Go eat a donut" is not a proper verbal defense. But an aggressive response can mean the difference between winning or losing.

In this situation, I was the victim. Usually the victim does not bring violence upon himself.

Strategically, in sports and war, it has been stated many times, "The best defense is a swift offense." Take control early on.

To sum up aggressiveness, "Do unto others as they would do unto you, but do it first and do it aggressively."

Have you ever seen a cat chase away a dog? A little guy fight off a big guy? Aggressiveness is the edge in any confrontation, offensive or defensive. The assailant does not expect aggressiveness in his victim, so you must catch him off balance by screaming a loud "No" or striking him hard.

The way in which you develop inner aggression is by visualizing someone attacking a family member. Harness that anger.

You can also pay attention to the daily newscasts. Current events revolving around terrorism and crimes against innocent people are enough to cultivate aggression. Consciously realize that the criminals you read and hear about have no right to prey upon innocent citizens. They are violating your personal comfort zone. They are scumbags, and you are justified—to the point of seeing red—in resenting their disgusting behavior.

The best-case scenario is when predators lose before they have a chance to advance.

The instant you know your assailant intends to do you serious physical harm, you must take action as quickly as you can. Always remember, you have the most control in the first 60 seconds of an attack. Your attacker chose you because you looked like easy pickings. You must immediately change his opinion of you. Your initial response can very well determine the outcome.

Stop for a moment, close your eyes, and think of a time in your life when you were so infuriated, so angry that your entire being was overcome with hate. That's what you must do, really. This is the kind of aggression that wins battles.

Survival Law 4: Use submissiveness

Fight or flight? That is the question.

When an unruly drunk started getting physical with the rest of the patrons, Bouncer Bob had to be called in. My job was to secure the safety of the wait staff, management, and patrons. Unfortunately, Jack Daniel's had polluted the mind and body of a trouble-maker who was already doped up on angeldust, which can give a person the strength of six men. When the drunk saw me approaching, his guard went right up. He had ferocity written all over his face. His next move was violence.

As cool as I could be, I approached the situation in a submissive manner and said to him, "You're the man, and everybody in here knows it." Buttering him up instead of escalating the situation allowed me to break his pattern—his train of thought. As he basked in his moment of glory, I reached down, grabbed his wrist, and twisted his arm tightly around his back, putting him in a position that allowed me to toss him out. My *acting* in a submissive manner was effective in getting him off guard.

You are in a situation where you are feeling vulnerable. Someone's following you, or a group of thugs is intimidating you. How do you respond? Do you blurt out obscenities and look intimidated? Or do you play-act in a submissive manner, all the while visualizing your offensive attack?

Sometimes a show of aggression, either verbal or physical, can prevent violence. Remember, you have the most control in the first minute. If your attacker is the least bit unsure of himself you have an advantage. Just make sure your aggressiveness is not just acting—make sure you can respond effectively.

Predators by nature consider you their prey. That's the natural hierarchy on the food chain theory. Their view of you is "below them" and "less than." In some cases when you respond with aggression this angers them.

So if you make the decision to offer resistance, give it everything you've got. Get real angry, explode, and go for the kill.

Sometimes it is more effective to act submissive.

In the animal world, dogs who are intimidated by a fiercer member of their species roll over and play dead. This act of submission is the animal's way of saying, "You win, you're the boss. I'm just a pawn, you're the king, I bow to you. You don't have to hurt me to prove your status."

Totally submitting to an aggressor goes against all my beliefs. However, play-acting submissiveness for the purpose of setting up your escape is sometimes necessary. If you are attacked, your submissive behavior may aid your escape, because your assailant may become smug over having dominated you and drop his guard. Little does he know you are reading this book.

On the other hand, submissiveness may make your attacker more sure of himself, thereby convincing him that he is safe to go ahead and violate you.

If you are going to act submissive, spend that time evaluating what you will do to debilitate this guy, if necessary.

Survival Law 5: Use decisiveness

"If you bring forth what is within you
What is within you will save you.
If you do not bring forth what is within you
What is within you will destroy you."

—**Rabbi Nochman**

Humans are decision-making machines, constantly evaluating, determining, concluding, and choosing. Every choice you have made in your life is part of the person you are right now. If you're not happy, start making better decisions. If you are excited about the future, good for you. In talking with people, I find that those who lack good decision-making skills say "I don't know" five to 100 times in a one-hour conversation. Pay attention to your self-talk.

Once people know how to make a decision to save their own lives, every other decision is relatively simple. The ability to make a decision is one of the benefits of being a human. Most animals are stuck with set instinctive ways and are limited in types of decisions or "choices" they can make. Because of our cultural conditioning, self-protection can be a tough choice. But I firmly believe that 10 percent of life is what happens to us, and the other 90 percent represents decisions to emotionally *react*—or properly *respond* to situations.

Most people become confused and disoriented in an assault. Their quick and efficient response in unlikely. It is extremely difficult to shift gears from being out for a casual stroll to having to fight off an attacker. However, in a situation in which your life is being threatened, you must have some ability to shift gears and take decisive action to fight back.

Decisiveness can be learned. You must rule out all conventional thinking and consider your attacker as an evil terrorist who must be eliminated. You must be able to inflict hurt. Possibly getting hurt and being injured are unknowns that you must not allow to get in the way of taking responsibility and protecting yourself and family.

Surges of emotion will dull any pain you might experience. Adrenaline and anger become fuel for your fire.

Let it make you rage.

Pain can help you fight.

An especially good way to train yourself to be decisive is to use visualization. Use the visualization techniques in the next chapter to see yourself fighting, hurting your assailant, and overpowering him—in spite of your own pain.

See him striking you. Visualize a knife in his hand. And then see yourself exploding with rage, ducking the knife, and tearing his throat out!

Survival Law 6: Use awareness

> **"Those who are first on the battlefield
> are at ease; those who are last
> on the battlefield are distressed."**
>
> **—Anonymous**

Awareness is consciousness, and consciousness is what living is all about. Living consciously is the essence of life. By paying attention, being alert, and becoming aware of your surroundings, you make life an adventure. Making awareness a habit lets you get so much more out of life. You will see things you never noticed before and you will start to see 10 times more of the good that life offers. For your safety, you will also see more of the bad.

Awareness is a natural animal ability, but like many natural abilities, it can be enhanced and improved. Once you accept that your everyday environment is, in fact, dangerous, you automatically sharpen your senses.

Here are two rules to live by:

> **1. Know what is going on behind you.**
> **2. Sharpen your senses to know
>   when anything is out of place.**

The great majority of victims of violent crime are taken by surprise. However, the person who anticipates an assault can avoid it or counter it.

Consider your pets for a moment. A dog or a cat that is awake, lying in its bed, or walking around the house or yard is not easily surprised. Even the slightest sounds get your pets' attention. The moment they sense something moving in the area around them they become alert to it. Their senses become piqued, their ears go up, and their body assumes a posture that puts them in ready mode. Animals are not thinking about what's on TV tonight or errands that need running; they're thinking safety, security, and protecting themselves and their home.

I suggest we get back to basics and think security.

Take note of anyone who is paying unwarranted attention to you or becomes alert when you appear. This is when you need to be on guard and be ready to defend yourself aggressively.

Some of this may sound like undue suspicion, but those who cultivate this kind of super-awareness find a new freedom. You will see more and hear more. Like awareness, a calm alertness is comforting.

Take a minute for safety.
Be aware.
Be alert.
Be ready.

My dad used to tell me, "Be good. Behave. Be careful." I always listened to one-third of his advice.

Survival Law 7: Use assertiveness

"Fortune sides with him who dares."

—Virgil, *Aeneid*

Assertiveness is the ability to exercise one's rights. It is not aggressiveness, which places your interests over others; it is personal awareness of what it is you want or need, and it is taking responsibility for seeing that your wants are met.

Awareness is the key, because you must first be in touch with your feelings before you can express those feelings honestly and comfortably and stand up for them.

Assertiveness is one of the most effective techniques for preventing assault. An assailant often tests a potential victim before determining that she or he is a candidate for attack. This testing may be in the form of moving very close to the prospective victim or touching to see how he or she reacts.

Assertive responses may be credited with preventing as many as four out of five assaults.

Assertiveness is largely a learned behavior. In our society men have traditionally been encouraged to be assertive while women have been taught to be submissive and accommodating. But anyone can learn to think and act assertively.

If the behavior does not come easily to you, begin to practice it in your everyday life. Only through practice will this essential quality be there when you need it.

Here are several ways to practice communicating assertiveness.

1. Examine your speech. Do you stutter, constantly rephrase sentences, let your sentences trail off into silence? Try speaking more slowly and choosing your words with attention to their exact meaning.
2. Is your voice soft and breathy? Project your voice from your diaphragm the way singers do.
3. Does your body belie your words with nervous movements or a tentative demeanor? Pay attention to your body. Focus on keeping it still and your movements purposeful.
4. You can also enroll in an assertiveness training or public speaking course.

Remember: assertiveness can be learned. Once you learn it you will find that it brings you many rewards as well as greater safety.

Survival Law 8: Use body language

**"If you know others and know yourself,
you will not be imperiled in a hundred battles;
if you do not know others but know yourself,
you will win one battle and lose the other;
if you do not know others and do not know
yourself, you will be imperiled in every battle."**

—Unknown

If you've ever participated in a sales program, you've learned that over 90 percent of communication is considered nonverbal. A person's physical body language—walk, posture, facial expressions, and eye contact—transmit 55 percent of that individual's communication. The pitch or tone of the voice accounts for 35 percent of communication, and the actual words transmit the remaining 10 percent.

Assertive body language, like anything else, can be learned by observing yourself and others.

1. Does the person appear nervous or relaxed, in control or fearful, aware or in a cloud? What is she doing with her body to give you that impression?

2. Does he exude control of his environment or appear skittish?

3. How does he hold his head—upright, appearing aware, or is he looking at the ground?

4. Does she look you in the eyes or does she look away when she talks to you?

5. Does he stand and sit straight, or does he slouch or hunch his shoulders?

6. Where does he have his hands? Are they in his pockets, closed into fists, or open?

7. How does she walk; purposefully with intent or aimlessly with hesitation?

Now observe yourself. How do you stand, sit, and walk? If you are expressing timidity with your body, consciously reposition it. Do this often, and assertive body language will become a habit. It will even change the way you think. You will become stronger, more confident, and more authoritative.

Survival Law 9: Use your voice

"A blow with a word strikes deeper than a blow with a sword."

—Robert Burton,
The Anatomy of Melancholy

What you say and how you say it can sometimes determine the outcome of a situation. Speak clearly and remain in control of your voice. An assertive voice is one that comes across convincingly—just as clenching one's teeth while talking convincingly comes across as anger.

Also perceived as assertive is raising the volume of your voice while maintaining a low pitch. Consider a common situation in which a child is acting out in a shopping mall and the mother wants to gain control without causing a scene. The manner in which she projects her anger while controlling her voice is one I've certainly experienced, and I can tell you first-hand it works!

I call this manner of speaking "charge neutral." I define charge neutral as being able to say what you want to without your voice betraying a rush, an edge, or a deadness in tone.

When a dog barks it is communicating on many different levels. It might be projecting basic communication across its neighborhood to other dogs. It might be expressing loneliness, excitability, happiness, or anger. Can you tell the difference between a dog barking a welcome and a dog barking a warning? I think a person should be able to tell the difference between friendliness and ferocity by the animal's tone and facial expression.

In some situations you need to come across with the same ferocity.

Because only 10 percent of communications are transmitted through our words, it is important that we be selective in using verbal defense. Words such as "Help" and "Rape" empower an attacker. Words such as "fire" and nine-one-one can attract greater attention to the situation. Words such as "no" and "stop" may cause your attacker to hesitate just long enough to give you the opportunity to strike or run. Profanities can also be effective.

When an attacker chooses you, he considers you weak and vulnerable. When you start screaming profanities as if you were disciplining a dog who had just bitten your hand, the body language, eye contact, and facial expression that accompany your reaction are what you need to project to repel an attacker.

By deliberately cultivating an assertive voice and the body language to match, you learn to project a strength that signals potential attackers that you are not a victim.

Survival Law 10: Use eye contact

"Women can give 'that look' that can turn Medusa to stone."

—Anonymous

Perhaps the most important part of body language is eye contact. In the animal world, dominance is often expressed by direct gaze; the animal that holds eye contact the longest wins. Human communication is very similar. If you feel uneasy or guilty in the presence of another, you are likely to avoid eye contact. In addition, women often feel—correctly—that maintaining eye contact with a stranger might be construed as an invitation to be approached.

If someone is taller than you, take a step or two back so you can hold your head level as you talk to him.

Varying degrees of eye contact can be interpreted in many ways. You can look at someone with welcome in your eyes or you can convey warning, hostility, or indifference. A stern, self-assured look can portray an air of confidence and project awareness of one's surroundings, reducing an attacker's element of surprise.

Keep in mind that nervousness can sometimes bring on a smile, which reduces the effect of assertiveness. If you respond with a nervous laugh or smile when you feel uncomfortable, practice not smiling or laughing in everyday situations until you develop a controlled look.

This does not mean you have to challenge someone to a staring match. You can look at the person in such a way as to show that you are aware of him but do not want any kind of physical or verbal engagement.

> **Remember: it's not the size of the person in the fight, it's the size of the fight in the person.**
>
> —Model Mugging (altered)

**The difference between most people
and someone who is successful
is not a lack of strength, not a lack of
knowledge, but rather a lack of will.**

:01

Chapter 4
The 10 Fundamentals of
Self-Defense

"Whether you think you can
or you can't—you are right."

—Henry Ford

The 10 Fundamentals of Self-Defense

Among the complex emotional traumas that people experience after someone assaults them, one common reaction is guilt for not having done all they could to stop the attack.

Self-defense experts estimate that in the face of an attack, a full 60 percent of victims become paralyzed with fear. Another 20 to 30 percent fight back to no avail, and 10 to 20 percent get away through physical self-defense, verbal persuasion, or just plain luck.

What would you do? More important, what *should* you do? Whether you should scream, hit, run away, or comply—the decision is not an easy one. Offering resistance is more effective for an escape than to just "let it happen."

Because of increasing violence on our nation's streets, people are becoming more concerned with knowing how to defend themselves. Perhaps you feel that you don't have the time to take formal martial arts or self-defense training. You may want merely to know some simple yet effective techniques "just in case."

You can practice a number of effective self-defense techniques on your own.

The moves you are about to learn are designed to divert an assailant and temporarily immobilize him so you have a chance to escape. Although they are simple techniques, they must be executed with determination. You cannot hold back out of fear that you will injure your attacker. You must be angry, vicious, ready to inflict pain.

For years, women have been told not to fight an assailant, that they were more likely to be injured if they resisted. But experts now say that although you should never fight for material goods—a purse or a watch—fighting back may be the only way to save yourself from injury or death.

If you're intimidated by the idea of defending yourself, or if you think you're too weak or too old, think again. Self-defense does not require years of martial arts training. Nor do the techniques require much physical strength. You simply have to be alert and prepared.

Your brain is your best weapon of self-defense.

A study of nearly a hundred women who were sexually assaulted—and who either were raped by a man or avoided being raped—reveals that those who escaped used many different defense techniques, including screaming and physical force. Pleading and crying were found to be ineffective defense strategies.

The study also shows that the sooner a woman defended herself, the more likely she avoided being raped. Although women who resist their attackers are more likely to suffer minor injuries such as scrapes and bruises, they are no more likely to suffer serious injury than women who do not resist.

Resisting may be easier said than done, however. Many people are unprepared for physical violence. Some may even feel uneasy or squeamish while reading parts of this book because of certain violent self-defense techniques described.

Often, women believe they could easily use physical violence if their children were threatened. Interestingly, although able to visualize seriously injuring or even killing an attacker to defend their children, many women admit they cannot conceive of defending themselves with the same ferocity.

**Violence in your own defense
is not only acceptable,
it is absolutely essential.**

Learning the techniques described in this book will greatly increase your chances of preventing or surviving an assault.

Do not let yourself become a victim.

If you are physically threatened or your life is at risk, it is NOT wrong to defend yourself by whatever means possible.

You have the right to fight back.

Many assailants are cowards, and many times an attack can be lessened or completely avoided by simply fighting back, verbally or physically or both.

Of course, some assailants become more dangerous when they are resisted, as I pointed out earlier. Let your instincts guide you— provided that you have honed those instincts by making yourself aware of the many self-defense techniques available to you and by practicing so that such techniques become instinctive.

The 10 Fundamentals of Self-Defense are:

1. keep the fighting spirit
2. adopt the fighting stance
3. gouge the eyes
4. stomp the foot
5. go for the throat
6. kick or knee the groin
7. slap the groin
8. use reversals and pins
9. take a minute to visualize
10. use your option to fight.

Initial confrontations can be as apparently nonthreatening as someone's asking for directions, or as vicious as someone's using a weapon with the element of surprise. In either situation, your response to your attacker can determine the outcome.

The 10 Laws of Survival (detailed in Chapter 3) along with the 10 Fundamentals of Self-Defense (which follow) give you viable options for increasing your security.

Fundamental 1: Keep the fighting spirit

This is a technique to use initially whenever you sense danger. If you are attacked you want to immediately offer resistance and penetrate your attacker's strike zones.

Strange as it may seem, your spirit in fighting should be determined and calm, as it is in everyday life. This determination is part of what I call "charge neutral."

Despite fear and anger, you must remain calm within, because only then can you think clearly enough to make the decision about whether to fight or submit.

**If you do decide to fight,
it must be a positive
and wholehearted choice.**

Keep your spirit settled and your body alert but relaxed. Nurture your wisdom so you can distinguish between good and evil. Study people one by one. When you cannot be deceived by human beings, you will be in tune with the powers of the universe. And you will be able to fight to protect yourself if you have to.

Fundamental 2: Adopt the fighting stance

(See Figure 4.1.)

To fight effectively:

1. Keep your head vertical, balanced on your neck, neither lowered nor raised nor twisted.
2. Do not wrinkle your forehead or brow.
3. Do not roll or blink your eyes, but keep them slightly narrowed.
4. Keep your nose straight and your nostrils slightly flared.
5. Stand straight, keeping your shoulders in line with the rest of your body.
6. Relax your shoulders, and slightly bend your knees.
7. Put strength into your legs from the knees to the tips of your toes.
8. Bend your elbows, keeping them close to your body, and open your hands, keeping your fingers slightly curled and pointing toward the sky.

This stance looks as if you are saying "Hey, I don't want any trouble," but it also lets you easily move in and strike any area of an attacker's body. The second he makes his move, lunge in and cut him down!

Figure 4.1. Adopt the fighting stance—Fundamental 2.

Fundamental 3: Fighting technique—Gouge the eyes

In an attack situation, you have to react instantly. If you practice certain basic fighting techniques thoroughly, you'll be ready. Practice them gently with a friend until each feels automatic.

Figure 4.2. Gouge the eyes—Fundamental 3.

Position	You must be able to see and reach the attacker's eyes.
Situation	The attacker faces you, then reaches to grab you. You have one arm free, possibly two.
	He is behind you and grabs your throat or "bear hugs" you, pinning your arms.
	He is on top of you, pinning you to the ground.
Technique	If your arms are pinned, stay calm, be patient. You'll eventually have a free arm.
	Jab your thumb or forefingers *hard* into one or both eyes.
	Be brutal. Use all your strength. Your life may depend on it.
	Don't stop until it's possible to get away.
Result	You will temporarily blind your assailant.
	He will take his hands off you to cover his eyes. Gouging the eyes is very painful—and very effective.
Common question	What if the assailant is taller than I am and I can't reach his eyes?
Answer	Go for the throat, stomp the instep of his foot, or wrench his groin (testicles). Be aggressive. Be flexible.
Practice	Visualize the move. Mentally practice it.
	Then practice by having someone grab you from the front or from behind and throw you on the ground.
	Take a self-defense course.

Fundamental 4: Fighting technique—Stomp the foot

(See Figure 4.3.)

Position	The attacker is in front of you.
	The attacker is behind you, "bear hugging" you and pinning your arms.
	The attacker has grabbed your arm or shoulder and has put his arm around you.
Technique	Stomp down *hard* on the top of his foot. Dig your heel into his foot. There are 26 bones in the human foot. You'll break at least one.
	Be brutal. Your life may depend on the effectiveness of your technique.
	Don't stop stomping until it is possible to get away.
Result	Sharp pain. Broken bones. You will destroy half your assailant's support system.
Common question	Does it matter how I place my foot?
Answer	Yes. Use your heel. Your heel can transmit the full force of your thigh and calf muscles.
Practice	Visualize the move. Then practice it by having your partner stand in different spots around you. In slow motion and gently, stomp on your partner's foot.
	Take a self-defense course.

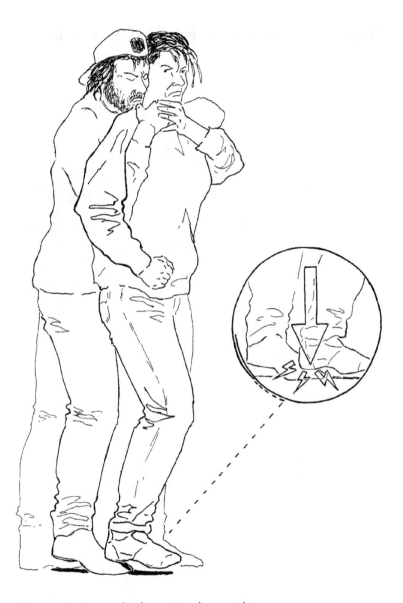

Figure 4.3. Stomp the foot—Fundamental 4.

Fundamental 5: Fighting technique—Go for the throat

Figure 4.4. Go for the throat—Fundamental 5.

Position	The attacker is standing off to your side or in front of you, about an arm's length away.
	The attacker is on top of you.
Situation	The attacker has reached out and is grabbing your clothes.
Technique	Open your hand, keeping your thumb curled tightly against your palm. Bend your fingers slightly. This puts tension in your hand and makes it strong.
	Chop to the attacker's throat. Strike with the palm down, hitting the attacker's windpipe with the side of your hand opposite your thumb.
	If a karate chop isn't possible, dig your thumb into the attacker's larynx and/or windpipe.
Result	A blow to the throat is very painful. It also collapses the windpipe, cutting off oxygen to the body. The attacker will be unable to move.
Common question	What if he's standing behind me?
Answer	Stomp his instep, slap his groin, gouge his eyes. Be flexible.
	Get angry! Be brutal!
Practice	Visualize the move. Have your partner grab your clothes or body in different places from different positions.
	Extend your arm to either chop or jab the throat. Pay close attention to the distance from your shoulder to the attacker's throat.
	Notice how far you have to extend your arm to reach his throat.
	Take a self-defense course.

Fundamental 6: Fighting technique—Kick or knee the groin

(See Figures 4.5 and 4.6.)

Fundamental 7: Fighting technique—Slap the groin

(See Figure 4.7.)

Figure 4.5. Kick the groin—Fundamental 6.

Position	The attacker is in front of you or behind you.
	The attacker is on top of you.
Situation	The attacker is coming toward you, trying to grab you. He may have already grabbed you.
	He may have knocked you down, or he may be strangling you from behind.
Technique	If you're lying on your back or standing up, kick the groin with your heel, toe, or instep. Any part of your foot will be effective.
	If the attacker wraps his arm around your throat from behind, point your chin toward his elbow so you can breathe, settle your weight, and slap his groin continuously until you can escape. If this doesn't work, find his eyes.
	If he's close enough, bring your knee straight up to his groin.
Result	Hitting or kicking the groin causes a great deal of pain. The attacker will double over and probably fall to the ground.
Common question	Does it really hurt that badly?
Answer	Yes! Really, *really* badly!
Practice	Visualize the moves. Practice them in slow motion with a partner.
	Take a self-defense course.

Figure 4.6. Knee the groin—Fundamental 6.

Figure 4.7. Slap the groin—Fundamental 7.

Fundamental 8: Use reversals

In the event that you find yourself in a situation where you cannot get out of your attacker's grip, when you feel you are overcome and restrained, all is not lost.

There are always options. They might not be immediately available to you, but when they are, take these options from zero resistance to 100 percent full combat.

This is called a full reversal.

Zero tension	Upon realizing you're overpowered, stop struggling and relax. Save your energy.
	Look as if you give up. This puts your attacker off guard.
	Show relaxation with your body. Look like a limp victim. This puts the attacker off guard.
	Remember that you can move faster with muscles that are relaxed.
Relax your mind	Breathe slowly and deeply. Filling your body with oxygen helps relax your body.
	Keep a keen eye on your next option. It may be only seconds, or it may be hours.
	But remain alert and positive so you can recognize and take advantage of the opening when it does come.
Stay in the moment	Stay in the moment. While waiting for your options stay connected to what's at hand.
	Don't get negative, don't let your mind drift.
	Observe every detail of your environment and look for weapons, escape routes, strike zones, and opportunities for distraction.

100% resistance	When your options open up, commit completely to disabling your attacker. Don't let up till you succeed! Go immediately from zero to 100 percent resistance with your body and voice. Scream loudly, ferociously and viciously! Like a cat backed in a corner, come out with claws sharp, eyes fierce, and fight to kill!
Use additional techniques	Lie. Make them an offer so you throw them off guard and give yourself an advantage.
	Act submissive. Let the assailant believe he's in control. This will put him off guard.
	Take control. Tell the assailant what to do. You might be surprised at how much you can get.
	When you're fighting, strike, jab, or gouge the eyes when you need to make space and time.
	Hit the groin. Go for the throat.
	Remember that your body always has more reserve energy to call upon than you believe it has.
	Use your assailant's fatigue to your advantage.

Patience and attitude + Full resistance = Reversal

Fundamental 9: Take a minute to visualize

In a course I took years back called Impact Model Mugging, still available in many large cities and towns, I learned a technique that I found extremely effective. Here it is, adapted from a course handout.

The best way to condition your mind is to mentally rehearse attacks and counterattacks.

This is called visualization. It is also known as "What ifs."

Experienced police officers use this technique. As they patrol the streets, approach a disturbance, or enter a suspicious building, they mentally rehearse what they would do if someone were waiting around the corner to attack, if a suspect were to draw a weapon, if they were walking into a set-up.

You can do the same thing when you take an evening stroll, walk past suspicious individuals, hear a noise in the night, or enter a parking garage. By consciously rehearsing plans to escape or to defend yourself, you condition your subconscious mind to react correctly under stress. The mind leads the body. Once the mind is trained to accurately visualize the successful application of a physical technique, the body is able to respond effectively in an actual attack.

Preparedness is not paranoia. It is a commonsense approach to urban survival.

You can use the same visualization technique that great athletes use, and you can develop the techniques of mind, body, and spirit necessary for your successful self-defense. You can also use visualization to condition your attitude.

Following are some mental exercises that will help you perfect your defense techniques.

Prepare for visualization	Find a quiet, comfortable place. Close your eyes. Breathe deeply and slowly. Let your thoughts come and go. Focus only on your breathing.
	Now visualize a blank screen. Choose to visualize yourself on this screen as a person of power.
Visualize each defense technique	Visualize yourself moving through each defense technique in slow motion.
	Follow through each motion with strong, graceful power.
Visualize each attack scenario	Picture yourself battling an attacker. Your mind is calm. You are determined to succeed.
	Every movement you make is strong, decisive, and focused. Visualize yourself defeating the attacker efficiently, smoothly, easily.
	Enjoy the victorious feeling you have as you stomp his head. Breathe deeply, and feel your victory in every part of your body.
Conclude each exercise	Visualize yourself in a place of beauty, comfort, and serenity. It is your own special place. You feel safe, content, warm, and happy. You are at peace with yourself.
	Breathe deeply, and open your eyes.
Use visualization every day	Constantly visualize potential danger and how you will deal with it.

**Athletes visualize themselves performing
an event in perfect form.
Then, when they compete, their
minds and bodies are prepared to excel.**

In addition to the meditative style of visualization, constantly visualize potential danger whenever one of the 10 Types of Personal Safety affects you (see Chapter 2).

For example, when you are out walking at night, visualize the possibilities of someone waiting around the corner to assault you. What if? What will you do? Where will you go? Where will you strike the individual?

I find that movies and television portray victims as being defenseless. When you are watching a victimization scene, visualize the victim fighting back. Get angry. Yell! Poke the attacker in the eye. Hit him in the groin!

This type of visualization is probably the most important technique, and one that is used most often to prepare for any dangerous situation. Use it before you enter your house, your car, and elsewhere.

Some of you may feel that this kind of vigilance is close to paranoia. Actually it produces the opposite result. Your senses become more acute. Eventually you see far deeper into everything that life offers.

**Visualizing the possibilities is what great
inventors, politicians, performers, athletes, and
other great minds of all time have in common.**

Fundamental 10: Use your option to fight

Street fights are hardly representative of a professional engagement by two skilled combatants in the ring. In fact, it's almost comical to watch two individuals thrashing about with little or no technique. Sometimes it's a lucky punch that wins the battle; sometimes one person just ends up on top of the other. Ultimately, attitude, decisiveness, determination, and aggression determine the outcome.

Attitude conquers size

When considering your options, consider this;
1. Nobody has the right to violate another!
    *   Humans have the right to live free from violence. All of us have a responsibility to ourselves and our families to fight back. This is fundamental.
    *   You are worth fighting for. Submitting and letting violence happen is a bad option. Fighting back increases your chances of survival.
2. Rule number one: Conventional thinking will get you killed.
    *   Humans want to trust one another. It's easier to get along if you have faith in people. However, trust can limit your ability to defend yourself.
    *   No matter what happens or what is said, the attacker is a filthy liar and should be dealt with accordingly.
3. Big or little, size is irrelevant.
    *   In a life or death situation, overcoming adversity is determined by the willingness to conquer your opponent.
    *   Know your options and know the most effective parts of your body available to you for debilitating the most available sensitive parts of the attacker's body.

4. Give it your all.
    *   This isn't a time to hesitate. If you are the sort of person who
        lets people go ahead of you when you drive or becomes
        confused at a rotary or a round-about, learn to get aggressive.
        In an attack, being nice—like letting others go first—is not
        an option. Get medieval on them. If someone were attacking
        your child, you'd respond with the needed ferocity.
    *   Be fully prepared to injure an assailant. If you are not
        resisting, he can do what he wants with you.

Studies have shown that the more people do to defend themselves as early as possible, the better the chance they will win. If you
are counterattacking, your assailant must then be concerned with
his own vulnerability. If it is one attacker or multiple attackers,
every technique described works on one assailant at a time. Hurt
one, then another. Before you know it, they'll all be running for
safety. If not, recoup and respond.

**"If you are threatened with attack, you may
respond immediately with decisive force."**

**—Former President Clinton,
outlining rules for U.S. troops**

Don't Quit

When things go wrong as they sometimes will,
When the road you're trudging seems all up hill,
When the funds are low and the debts are high,
And you want to smile, but you have to sigh,
When care is pressing you down a bit,
Rest if you must but don't quit.

Life is queer with its twists and turns,
As every one of us sometimes learns,
And many a failure turns about,
When he might have won had he stuck it out.
Don't give up though the pace seems slow,
You may succeed with another blow.

Success is failure turned inside out,
The silver tint of the clouds of doubt,
And you never can tell how close you are,
It may be near when it seems so far,
So stick to the fight when you're hardest hit,
It's when things seem worse that you must not quit.

—Author Unknown

**If it is to be,
It is up to me.**

Chapter 5
Invest in Your Self-Defense

The spirit, the will to win, and the will to excel are the things that endure.

:01

Invest in Your Self-Defense

A wide variety of crime prevention and personal safety products are available to you.

Here is a summary of the most widely used types of self-defense devices you can use when you are out walking in public, together with my suggestions for their proper use. I'll also give you a brief overview of some of the products that are available for protecting yourself and your property when you're at home, in your car, or staying in a hotel.

As you'll notice, there are advantages and disadvantages associated with the use of these products.

Devices to carry

1. Whistles

A whistle is probably the most inexpensive device for scaring off a potential attacker. High quality whistles can be purchased at sporting goods stores or other retail outlets. Make sure you purchase a sturdy metal whistle that is capable of emitting a loud noise.

When carrying a whistle, it is best if you either attach it to a bracelet or hold it in your hand. If you wear it on a chain around your neck, you may have trouble quickly grasping it and placing it in your mouth.

2. Personal alarms

These emit loud, piercing noises, much louder than whistles. They tend to be small, often the size of a pack of cigarettes, and they can easily be carried by hand or attached to a belt or purse strap.

You need to carry the alarm so you can easily activate it.

Because a personal alarm doesn't inflict any pain upon an attacker, any psychological or moral misgivings you might have about using a gun or other protection device aren't there. The lack of real protection is also the major drawback of any type of alarm.

In most instances, the noise should scare off an attacker. If the attacker is brazen enough to continue, however, no alarm or whistle can give you any real defense.

Personal alarms use either battery power or aerosol spray to produce a loud siren or whistle. Pulling a pin or depressing a switch activates such alarms. The sound—in the 100 to 130 decibel range—is about the maximum noise the ear can take without being damaged.

Some personal alarms are equipped with flashing lights that attract further attention from passersby. Some models are also equipped with straps or switches that allow you to attach them to doors or windows. In that regard, they can be used in hotel rooms to frighten away burglars or attackers.

In my opinion, virtually any model that emits a sound in the range of 110 to 130 decibels that can be clipped to your belt will work just fine.

3. Self-defense sprays

The use and popularity of such sprays has grown immensely in recent years. They are legal now in virtually every state, they can be easily carried, and although they can cause temporary and very painful discomfort to an assailant, they do not cause permanent injury. However, environmental conditions—wind, in particular— can limit their effectiveness.

You need to be aware of certain factors before purchasing any spray. Whereas using a self-defense spray does not require the same degree of knowledge, training, or judgment that the proper use of handguns or other dangerous weapons requires, you should nevertheless look into whether or not your local police department or any community group offers training and advice in using such sprays. You don't want your first "hands-on" experience to take place when you're facing an actual attack. The same advice applies, of course, to the purchase of any self-defense device.

There are a number of considerations associated with buying a particular type or brand of self-defense spray, too.

Size of canister. Try to avoid any spray that is sold in a very small canister. Canisters generally range in size from 15 grams to 60 grams. While their convenient size may make them appealing, a small canister has a very limited spraying capacity. The small size also limits their range, as well as making them difficult to handle and aim in a tense situation.

Chemical source. Be aware, too, of the chemical compositions of these sprays and their different characteristics. Essentially all self-defense sprays are formulated with one of the following three basic compounds:

- CS: orthochlorobenzalmalonitrile;
- CN: alphachloroacetaphenone; or
- OC: oleoresin capsicum.

Spra 7ys such as tear gas are CS- and CN-based. They work by causing severe irritation to membrane tissues. While they can be effective in subduing a criminal, several major disadvantages are associated with their use.

The amount of time necessary for a CS- or CN-based spray to

take effect can leave a criminal with enough time to complete a deadly attack from close range. Also, psychotic individuals or people whose senses have been dulled through the use of alcohol or other drugs may feel no effect at all from such sprays.

On the other hand, OC-based sprays, such as pepper sprays, cause tissue inflammation rather than irritation. That makes them more potent and effective, even on individuals whose senses are already numbed. A spray of an OC-based solution typically causes a person's eyelids to swell shut and breathing tissues to expand rapidly. Momentary blindness and extreme shortness of breath result.

Unlike CS- and CN-based sprays, which are derived from manufactured chemicals, OC-based sprays are derived from various hot pepper plants. The effects of OC-based sprays also wear off sooner than the other sprays—usually within 20 to 45 minutes.

Because of all those factors, I recommend sprays that contain OC.

Two other factors to consider when purchasing a spray are the concentration of the inflammatory agent and the spray pattern in which it is dispersed.

Potency. Because OC-based sprays are derived from hot peppers, the potency of the hot pepper plant from which that particular brand of spray is derived can be more important than the level of concentrate itself. In other words, a spray that contains a 10 percent concentrate derived from a relatively mild pepper might not be as effective as one with only a 1 percent concentrate of an especially hot pepper.

The best way to measure the potency of a particular pepper spray is by the number of SHUs that the particular product contains. SHU stands for Scoville Heat Unit.

Spray patterns. There are generally three types of spray patterns:

- stream patterns;
- cone-shaped mists; and
- fogger patterns.

Stream droplet sprays have the greatest range: up to 20 feet. They also are less likely to be affected by breezes or gusts of wind. Aiming such a spray, however, requires a much greater degree of accuracy.

Cone mists, as the name suggests, create a mist and a wider protective barrier. However, they generally have only half the range of a stream spray and are more easily affected by breezes.

Fogger sprays offer many of the advantages of both stream and cone mist sprays. Foggers work somewhat like a fire extinguisher in that they have a range of up to 25 feet. They also are quite potent. Their main drawback is that the number of "shots" in a fogger spray container is less than what can be found in stream or cone mist models.

What specific brand or product do I recommend? When out in public, you will do well to have a spray that carries the original Mace® brand product identification fortified with both CN and OC. It delivers a stream spray, and I've seen one 4-foot 11-inch woman knock down six large men with one sweeping spray. Its compact physical design features a belt clip and a flip-top safety cap, making it easy to carry and use. I also like the combination of OC and CN concentrations: if the pepper spray doesn't get them, the tear gas will.

For the home, I suggest an OC fogger model, also manufactured by the company that makes Mace. Have a canister in your bedroom, bathroom, kitchen, and by the front door.

4. Stun guns (electrical defense units)

A stun gun is a hand-held device that features a pair of electrical contacts. The current arcing from the contacts creates the "stun."

Stun guns are battery-powered and carry currents up to 600,000 volts. They can immobilize an assailant for 5 to 10 minutes, but they do not cause permanent injury. They are operated by the contacts being pressed against an assailant's body for several seconds.

A stun gun is activated by pulling a pin or flipping a switch. The loud, crackling noise emitted can itself be very intimidating. There is no danger of your being shocked by pressing the gun against an assailant; the current concentrates in the assailant's tissues.

There are two very crucial considerations you should be aware of when using a stun gun.

1. You have to be very close to an attacker before you can use it. This puts you in immediate contact with the attacker, increasing your risk if his primary weapons are his hands.

2. You have to be strong enough to hold a stun gun against your attacker's body for several seconds, otherwise your attacker could tear the stun gun out of your hands and use it against you.

If you plan on purchasing a stun gun, I suggest that you purchase a model no larger in diameter than 5.5 inches by 2.5 inches, with a current of 100,000 to 500,000 volts or more.

My recommendation is the Omega® brand because of its compact design, high quality plastic, and potent shock.

5. Handguns

Despite the lethal power of handguns against an attacker, I do not recommend that you carry one. To begin with, the purpose of this book is to provide you with the advice you need for avoiding an attack or for disabling an attacker so you can get away.

Displaying a gun forces you to instantly consider whether you're really willing to take another person's life. If a criminal senses that you are hesitant to use such deadly force, the gun could easily be wrested from you and used against you.

The use of handguns also requires specialized training as well as keen judgment as to when the use of such force is appropriate. If you wound or kill an attacker, a jury could decide that you used excessive force in defending yourself. Also, carrying a concealed gun almost always requires a special permit.

You may have heard the tragic news story about the man who shot and killed his own stepdaughter, believing he was confronting a burglar. That morning the man had gone to his office, where he received a phone call from the security company reporting that the alarm at his house had been tripped. He went home, found the front door unlocked, and got his .38-calibre handgun. As he began to search each room, the stepdaughter, hearing someone else in the house, hid in her bedroom closet. When the man reached his stepdaughter's room, he opened the closet door, saw someone move, and pulled the trigger.

Unfortunately, this is not an isolated incident. The scenario depicted here is all too common today. I'm sure that with 20/20 hindsight, the stepfather might have chosen to fill the closet with a fog of tear gas, causing the intruder to temporarily choke, gag, and lose sight. Please understand that tear gas and pepper spray are temporary. A bullet is forever.

6. Knives or other lethal hand-held weapons

As with guns, the use of a knife requires the willingness to kill or wound another person. It also escalates the seriousness of the confrontation.

Using a knife or other hand-held lethal weapon (a blackjack, for example) requires that you be willing to engage in close, physical combat with a criminal. Your weapon could be taken away and used against you. Many of the same legal issues that apply to the possession and use of handguns apply to knives or other weapons.

7. Products for protecting valuables on your person

Certain products are specially designed to protect your valuables when you're out on the street. There are concealed wallets, or body safes, in which you can place your money or credit cards. These pouches can be strapped around your ankle, attached to an undergarment, or slipped over your shoulder under a jacket or coat.

There are also portable property alarms that can be attached to camera cases, skis, bicycles, suitcases, golf bags, or other valuable items that you may want to briefly set down in a restroom or terminal. These alarms are sensitive to vibration and will sound if the item is moved. These alarms are activated and deactivated through the use of a combination or code, or by remote control.

Home security products

1. Lighting

One unobtrusive means for protecting your home is to use a motion-detecting lighting system. Such a system illuminates the perimeter of your house, functioning by means of motion-sensitive lights mounted near doors or windows. When a person comes within range of the sensor, the lights automatically go on. Such systems can be a great deterrent whether you're at home or away.

2. Alarm systems

I won't go into any great detail here: numerous books can provide you with ample information about the costs and merits of many specific systems. Instead, I will provide you with some general background that will help you become familiar with the types of systems available.

Burglar alarms deploy two general types of sensor: perimeter and interior. Perimeter sensors become activated when a door or window is broken or opened. Interior sensors are activated by either motion or body heat when someone is present in a room or corridor. The more complete alarm systems feature a combination of both perimeter and interior sensors.

Another factor is the difference between hard-wired and wireless systems. Hard-wired systems have all the sensors wired to a central control unit. With wireless systems, the individual sensors are attached to small battery-operated transmitters that send a radio signal to the central control unit.

Hard-wired systems require more effort to install, but tend to be more reliable than wireless systems; there's no need to replace batteries and no worries about any possible signal interference.

Another consideration in selecting between these two types may be the cost in relation to how long you plan to live at your current residence.

Some systems can be linked to a central monitoring service that immediately notifies the police in the event of a break-in.

3. "Peep hole" viewers

Peep hole viewers are small wide-angle lenses that are installed through the core of your door. They enable you to see who's standing outside before you open the door. Their size is between 1/4 inch and 1/2 inch.

4. Door chains

Door chains are effective only if they are securely mounted to a door and its frame with long, thick screws. Otherwise they provide a false sense of security, because a strong impact can often cause the mounting brackets to break loose from either the door or the door frame.

5. Window locks

Some of the newer manufactured windows come with built-in locks or stops that prevent a window from being opened from the outside. Many of them allow the window to be left slightly open for ventilation.

There are also "do-it-yourself" kits that allow you to install pins or locks in existing window frames. With any such devices, be sure that they can easily be opened or removed from the inside in the event of a fire or other emergency.

Automobile security products

1. Alarms

As with home alarms, a variety of products are available in a range of prices and levels of sophistication. In many ways they work on the same principles as home alarms.

Breaking a window, opening a door, or opening a hood or trunk lid, for example, will cause some alarms to sound. Others have motion sensors that detect the presence of someone within the car's interior. Some sensors sound an alarm if the automobile is subjected to any vibration, such as being lifted by a tow truck.

Some alarms feature combinations of the above safety features. Others disable a car's electrical system or fuel supply.

The complexity of a security system also influences the degree of expertise required for its installation. Some systems that sense only motion or vibration can be easily dash-mounted, getting power from the car's cigarette lighter. More sophisticated models require more extensive wiring and installation of sensors.

2. Wheel locks

Such devices feature long shafts with arms that hook around the steering wheel. Once wedged and locked into place, these devices prevent someone from turning the steering wheel more than a few degrees in either direction.

Although these devices may not stop a seasoned or very determined automobile thief who is equipped with a hacksaw or other tools, they do serve as a deterrent.

Travel security products

1. Locks

Portable locks can be used to secure windows in your hotel or motel room. Other locks can also be inserted between a door and its frame as an additional precaution against intruders.

2. Alarms and door stops

As mentioned earlier, some personal alarms can be attached to windows or doors. There are also wedge-shaped door stops equipped with battery-powered alarms that sound if anyone tries to force open your door.

Self-defense classes

Despite the wide variety of crime prevention and personal safety devices available, it is important to recognize one fact:

___

You cannot rely solely on any device.

___

Knowing the tips and techniques I have been describing throughout this book will improve your odds for both avoiding an assault and getting away unharmed.

Undoubtedly you have been noticing as you read this book that I frequently recommend your taking a self-defense course. I want you to seriously consider this resource because it not only gives you a range of specific skills to use in a variety of threatening situations, but also supports the kind of attitude change that builds the confidence, self-esteem, and assertiveness that tells a potential assailant to look elsewhere—you are not a victim.

Hence, the most important thing to learn in such a class is how to prepare yourself mentally to attack an assailant with ferocity and determination. This can be extremely difficult for some people to do because most of us—and especially women—have been culturally conditioned not to fight. Any self-defense course *must* teach you to overcome this conditioning and to become vicious and unmerciful when the situation requires it.

The course must also teach you *practical* fighting tactics. Even years of karate will not necessarily prepare you for a real-life confrontation.

Many types of self-defense courses are available. To find the course that's right for you, contact your nearest rape crisis center or your local police department's crime prevention unit. Or look in the Yellow Pages under "karate" or "martial arts instruction."

I recommend "Model Mugging," a real-life, streetwise self-defense course that is offered in about 30 cities across the nation. The course lasts 25 hours and costs about $500.

No matter what your age or physical condition, you can find a course that teaches the techniques you can perform. And enroll your children in a self-defense course, too.

:01

Chapter 6
Prevent Identity Theft

"Good people do not need laws to tell
them to act responsibly, while
bad people find a way around the laws."

—Plato

Prevent Identity Theft

When you think of a burglar, you think dark clothing, black hat, and the tools of his trade—typically a crowbar and a bag to carry the loot. A new kind of thief uses tools of the trade that consist of your everyday transactions. Each transaction of yours requires you to share personal information: bank, credit-card numbers, Social Security numbers, name, address, and phone numbers. An identity thief takes a part of your personal information and uses it without your knowledge to commit fraud or theft. The most common ruse is to use your personal information to open a credit-card account.

Can you completely prevent identity theft? No. But you can reduce your risk by managing your personal information wisely, cautiously, and with heightened sensitivity. Criminals have concluded that identity theft is a low-risk, high-yield crime. They know that any document of any kind can be counterfeited. They live as if they were you, and commit crimes as if they were you. This type of crime is affecting hundreds of thousands of people a year.

How does a thief obtain an ID? By buying an identity, stealing an identity, creating an identity, or piecing together an identity.

- Buying an identity can cost only a few hundred dollars. The thief buys an identity from someone who has previously pieced together someone else's identity, then adds his own photo to it.

- Stealing an identity means acquiring someone's personal information in a variety of ways and using it fraudulently.
- Creating a false identity means just picking a Social Security number out of the air and building an identity from there.
- Piecing together an identity involves research and persistence on the thief's part.

Here is a note I received from a friend who was victimized:

Friends,

As many of you know, back in October 2001 I had my mail stolen and a woman had assumed my identity with my SSN and used some convenience checks issued by credit card companies. It took many hours to cancel all my cards and change the account numbers on my other money accounts, fill out affidavits of fraud, get charges reversed, contact the 3 credit bureaus, put a fraud alert on my SSN, fill out a police report, fill out the Postal Inspector report, get my landlord to purchase and install a new SECURE mailbox, and work with a store manager where the woman was picking up merchandise under my name with those checks to get her arrested.

On November 8, 2001, Yvette Harris was arrested by the Cambridge Police at that store and has been in jail up until February 19, 2002. Yesterday, I was at the Cambridge courthouse as a witness/victim for the Commonwealth vs. Yvette Harris. This is the woman who stole my identity and committed fraud against me. She got a 4-1/2-year suspended sentence after serving a little over 3 months in jail. That means if she violates her probation in any way she immediately goes to jail for 4-1/2 years. This was her plea bargain for pleading guilty to all

*counts: committing fraud, forgery, and identity theft, and
resisting arrest. She has 45 prior convictions and may go
right back to doing it again.*

*I just wanted to let you all know how I handled it and
how it turned out. Hopefully, from this incident you'll all
be more aware of identity theft in your own community.
First step is to have a secure mailbox; next is to keep
track of activity on your credit cards and investment
accounts; lastly is to know the steps to take if you lose
your wallet or notice that you are missing some mail. This
woman could have ruined my credit rating, which could
have taken years to fix. As working people, we all try to
establish ourselves financially for the future, and with the
growing trend of this type of crime, we should all be more
aware of how easily it could be taken away.*

Kim

What makes an identity?

All a thief needs is a name, Social Security number, date of birth,
address, and mother's maiden name. With a combination of these
parts of your identity a thief can become you. By using two or three
of these facts, a thief can piece the rest together. Once the thief has
obtained this biographical information, he or she creates a parallel
identity and runs up credit under the "twin's" bio.

Legal forms of ID in circulation are actually part of the problem.
Over the years, government bureaucracies have created the foundation for an identity thief to capitalize on the overabundance of
legal papers. For example, there are 49 valid versions of Social
Security cards. How would a bank representative, for example,
know what was real and what was fake? There are 14,000 types of
birth certificates. How could a school administrator granting ad-
mission—or a Department of Motor Vehicles employee furnishing
a driver's license—be able to tell, from a birth certificate and a

Social Security card, whether the identification was real or fake?

More than 200 forms of driver's licenses are currently in circulation. That averages to four different kinds of licenses per state. How could anyone responsible for confirming identity possibly be able to confirm a ruse? The ability to absolutely confirm the identity of an individual through documentation has been spinning out of control for years.

Biometric technology, including fingerprints, iris scans, facial recognition, DNA, and dental records are the only true identifiers. We are still years away from biometric technologies becoming standard identifiers. Until then, any unscrupulous person with enough savvy can compile, steal, or create an identity with little effort.

How it works

Ways in which an ID is acquired include the simple to the complex. Loss of belongings — such as a wallet or purse containing credit, bank, Social Security cards, and blank checks — is all a thief needs to become you.

Misdirected mail or post office screw-ups can send tax documents, bank loan applications, and other revealing documentation to a savvy thief.

Dumpster diving

Dumpsters at public or private locations can turn up a treasure-trove of resources for the thief. Think of the detailed documentation that can get into the wrong hands if not disposed of properly by any of the following entities — all of which currently possess personal information about you:

- financial agencies: banks, creditors, stockbrokers, investment managers
- utilities: gas or oil heat, water, electric, phone, cell phone
- memberships: video clubs, gyms, civic groups, homeowners'

and time-share associations
- vendors: suppliers, contractors, freight carriers, realtors
- services: mechanics, dry cleaners, janitors, day care, blood banks, hairdressers, hospitals, physicians, attorneys
- government agencies: IRS, Bureau of Vital Statistics, Social Security Administration, law enforcement, DMV
- insurance companies: health, dental, auto, home, life, business
- employer
- landlord.

Hacking

Computer hacking via the Internet into banks, credit accounts, utilities, credit bureaus, and government agencies are high-tech ways of getting personal information by the boatload. A hacker living overseas hacked into the computers of a Kansas bank, gaining access to 18,000 names, accounts, and Social Security numbers. Thiefs posing as a major auto manufacturer gained access through Experians system and stole credit reports of 13,000 people. In New York, authorities busted the largest identity theft ring in history. Records from a credit reporting company were sold for $50 to $75 each; as a result, the accounts of unsuspecting victims were raided by identity thieves in an amount upwards of $2.5 million.

Inside job

Dishonest employees and gangs are becoming increasingly savvy to confidential customer data. Employees at banks, credit unions, and reporting companies have been discovered with affiliations to gangland activities. Gang members are applying for jobs where they have direct access to customer information.

Social engineering

Thieves routinely pose as you, your spouse, bill collectors, fellow employees, bank reps, government agencies, landlords, or utility agents. They call financial institutions, utilities, employers, and any other private or public entities that have information about your accounts to try to sway employees into providing them with it.

For example, the identity thief may pose as you, saying that he misplaced his account number and giving your Social Security number, which he obtained from other means. This often convinces the employee that the call is legitimate. If the thief doesn't get the information he wants from the first employee he speaks with, he continues to call until he gets someone on the phone who does. With each call, each employee gives out a little bit of additional information. Each little bit is used by the identity thief in follow-up calls, further gaining the trust of the employee taking the call. Eventually, the thief extracts every bit of info he needs.

Putting the parts together

Thieves easily get your name, address, and phone number. Once they obtain your Social Security number through dozens of different ways, they're in the best position to become you. They establish an address other than yours. They start with easy credit, such as pre-approved credit card offers they steal from your mail. They might seek out lenders who grant instant approvals or who post signs reading "No Credit Report Required." Next, they obtain multiple cell phone accounts, one as "you" and another as your employer or "references." They obtain toll-free numbers under your name and direct incoming calls toward a cell phone line, thereby disguising the line as a business line.

Then they go online to create a free email account under your name, such as Your.name123@anyemail.com. All this gives the identity thieves more credibility. Now they go to work on establishing false IDs. They can go online to a variety of foreign Websites and order state drivers' licenses. Or they can create realistic drivers' licenses using their own computers, the right software, new high-tech printers, digital cameras, and laminators.

Now they take it to the next level. They get a bank account under your name. They order checks under your name. When the checks arrive they go on mad spending sprees and bounce checks all over town. They rent plush apartments and put down the necessary deposit with bogus checks. The landlord spends months trying to evict the identity thief under your name. They also open utilities, gas, and electric accounts in your name. They fill their apartments with stolen goods. They deal drugs. They take out loans and buy cars, which they make no payments on. They create counterfeit checks based on accounts from local businesses. They make these checks payable to your name. They cash these checks at the same banks where the checks are drawn. They get jobs posing as you, a doctor, lawyer, pharmacist, or whatever. They work for a week and rob the place blind while acquiring more identities.

This cycle goes on, and on, and on, for as long as possible, until the bill collectors or law enforcement authorities knock on *your* door looking for *you*, and demand payment or seek to arrest you for the crimes of the identity thief.

Victim red flags

You might be a victim of identity theft if you are denied credit for no reason, discover wrong information on your credit report, your mail stops arriving or certain bills or statements don't arrive, bills from companies you've never done business with show up in your mailbox, collection agencies call you for nonpayment, you get arrested for something you didn't do, or you are denied employment as a result of a background check.

If this happens to you, get moving fast.

Victim impact and effects

Arrests, false convictions

A woman from Alabama spent 10 days in jail after an identity thief wrote counterfeit checks under her name. What led to the victim's arrest was a traffic violation. When she was pulled over, the police ran her license and saw that a warrant had been issued for her name. Her begging and pleading did her no good, and she was arrested because her name had been used on counterfeit checks.

Another woman, pregnant, checked into a hospital under a stolen identity, gave birth, and disappeared, leaving the baby. The doctors determined it was a crack baby and forwarded the information to law enforcement. The police went to the home of the woman whose ID had been stolen, assuming she was the mother who'd given birth at the hospital. The victim was out shopping, but her kids were home with a baby sitter. The children were taken into protective custody. When the mother came home she was arrested. It took many hours for the victim to be exonerated and released, and to get her children back.

Another women with perfect credit who'd never had any trouble with the law got a call from Bank of America, asking why she had not made payments on her new truck. She'd never bought a truck. A felon had stolen her identity, rang up over $50,000 of debt, was subsequently arrested for trafficking 3,000 pounds of marijuana, and was booked and jailed under the victim's name. After 500 hours of police legwork, thousands of dollars in personal expense, and hours of pleading with law enforcement personnel, she was cleared — but still scared.

Each case consumes hundreds of hours of cleanup, with considerable trauma and financial expense for the victim, including attorney's fees and lost time from work. The FTC states that a victim's out-of-pocket expense averages $1,100.

Credit denied

Each instance of nonpayment and delinquency is held against the victim's credit until each is rectified. In the meantime, the victim's legitimate attempts to purchase a car or home or rent an apartment are denied.

Employment refused

If a potential employer does a background check on you for your credit rating, employment history, or criminal record and determines from the information that you are unsuitable for hire, you have to prove your innocence. Just the circumstance of having been a victim can be enough to turn off a potential employer, even though doing so is illogical, unethical, and illegal.

Psychological trauma

Having a twin walking around and soiling your good name feels like having your soul stuck in a garbage disposal. A thief can take an entire life's good work and turn it to mud in a short period of time. Even years after victims have cleaned up the mess, residue of the victimization shows up in uncorrected databases when least expected. You could be on vacation a year later in the Bahamas, have your identity recognized in a computer system, and be denied services.

Prevention dos and don'ts

1. Do check credit reports at least semiannually.
2. Do check spouse's credit reports.
3. Do lock mailbox.
4. Do shred all throwaway documents.
5. Do memorize PINs, passwords, SS#s.
6. Do change passwords semiannually.
7. Do photocopy all documents in your wallet/purse.
8. Do secure all legal documents, account numbers, tax records, cancelled checks.
9. Do opt out of pre-approved credit card offers and destroy pre-approved credit cards.
10. Do place mail in secure outgoing mailboxes.
11. Do call the post office if you go more than four days without mail.

12. Do pay attention to the delivery dates of all bills.

13. Do pay close attention to bank and credit card statements.

14. Do reconcile bills and statements diligently in a timely manner.

15. Do pay attention to the expiration date of credit cards and watch for prompt arrival of replacement cards.

16. Do sign all new cards immediately.

17. Do destroy black carbon credit receipts.

18. Do avoid using Social Security numbers for accounts whenever possible.

19. Do initiate passwords for all accounts, especially credit cards.

20. Do have bank-ordered checks sent to the bank, not your home.

21. Do get removed from the Direct Marketing Association lists (see "Resources" on page 142).

22. Do be cautious ordering online and via mail order.

23. Do ask all public and private entities about their policies for disposal of records.

24. Do be aware of people standing close to you at an ATM and "shoulder surfing".

25. Don't leave your wallet or purse in your car.

26. Don't carry your Social Security card, birth certificate, or passport unless necessary.

27. Don't carry more than two credit cards.

28. Don't keep PINs and passwords in your wallet or purse.

29. Don't use common passwords such as mother's maiden name, birth date, last four digits of your SS#, phone number, pet's or kid's name, or any series of consecutive numbers.

30. Don't have SS# or driver's license numbers printed on checks.

31. Don't write account numbers on the outside of envelopes.

32. Don't list yourself in the telephone book.

33. Don't communicate personal information over the phone, such as SS#, birth date, mother's maiden name, or credit card numbers.

34. Don't have bank-ordered checks delivered to your mail box.
35. Don't lend credit cards to people who won't be as responsible as you.
36. Don't leave receipts lying around.

Victim's to-do list

1. Call the FTC and ask for its "Good Name" packet.
2. Document every conversation and contact you have.
3. Contact the fraud departments of the three major credit bureaus and initiate fraud alerts.
4. Order credit reports and review them.
5. Contact and close all credit, utility, bank, and credit accounts opened fraudulently.
6. File a police report and send it to all creditors and agencies involved.
7. Contact your local postal inspector and the Postmaster General.
8. If checks were used fraudulently contact your bank's check fraud services.
9. If phone service was begun under your name call the FCC.
10. Call the Social Security Administration.
11. Call the U. S. Bankruptcy Administration to see if your ID has been filed.
12. Check your criminal record to see if charges are filed.
13. When you correspond with agencies and businesses to clear up ID fraud, take your mail to the post office and mark it RETURN RECEIPT REQUESTED.
14. Once you start encountering roadblocks, consult an attorney

Resources

To be removed from direct mail lists:
Direct Marketing Association Mail Removal List
POB 9008
Farmingdale NY, 11735
www.the-dma.org

To be removed from telemarketing lists:
DMA Telephone NO CALL List
POB 9014
Farmingdale, NY 11735

To opt out of pre-approved/pre-screened credit card offers:
1-888-5-OPTOUT

To remove email address from spam:
www.e-mps.org

To have the Postal Service hold your mail up to 30 days:
1-800-275-8777 (during business hours)

To report mail fraud to the U.S. Postal Inspector:
www.usps.gov/websites/depart/inspect
(this alerts your local postal inspector as well)

To report check fraud:
National Check Fraud Service, 1-843-571-2143
SCAN, 1-800-262-7771
Telecheck, 1-800-710-9898
Crosscheck, 1-707-586-0551
International check, 1-800-526-5380

To report telephone fraud:
FCC, www.fcc.gov or 1-888-CALL-FCC

To report fraud affecting credit / to request a credit report:

Experian (formerly TRW)
POB 1017
Allen, TX 75013
1-888-397-3742

Equifax
POB 740241
Atlanta, GA 30374
1-800-685-1111 or 1-800-525-6285

Trans Union
POB 97328
Jackson, MS 39238
1-800-680-7289 or 1-800-888-4213

Federal Trade Commission (FTC)
Identity Theft Clearing House
Washington DC, 20580
1-877-ID-THEFT
www.consumer.gov/idtheft [also covers phone fraud]
1-877-FTC-HELP

Other contacts:

Social Security Administration (SSA)
POB 17768
Baltimore, MD 21235
1-800-269-0271 or 1-800-772-1213

U.S. Bankruptcy Administration
www.usdoj.gov/ust

"Half of this game is
90 percent mental."

—Yogi Berra

:01

Conclusion

Much has been covered in this complete guide to personal security. We all know that repetition is the mother of skill, so I encourage you to read and re-read this book. Slowly you must start to incorporate the different techniques into your mind, body, and soul. Adopting the following three principles will help you to fully integrate the information covered in this book.

1. Pay attention to your body language. This includes having a full understanding of the way you walk, making sure you embody a walk that "means business," using strong eye contact when necessary, and speaking assertively.

2. Be aware. This includes being fully aware of your body language and everyone else's, being aware of your surroundings, and knowing what is happening 50 to 100 feet around the perimeter of your body at all times. Know what is a potential danger, which means paying particular attention to anything that is out of place.

3. Listen to your intuition, which is perception beyond the physical senses. It is that sensory system which operates without any data from your five senses. With the perception of a five-sensory human, each of us exists in a totally physical universe. With the perception of a multisensory human, our universe becomes alive, conscious, intelligent, and compassionate. If we pay attention to this power inside and around us, we receive the signals of opportunity and of danger in time to seize the moment.

Ironically, our development grows at a more rapid pace when we put aside the fast-paced hustle and bustle of daily activity to pay more attention to our peace of mind and to become in tune with our sixth sense.

Plain and simple, if your intuition is screaming that something does not feel right, don't discount that feeling. Recognize it, pay full attention to it, and then act upon it.

Remember, you create your reality with your intentions. If you intend to be safe, so shall you be safe. If you choose the victim role in life by not taking responsibility for your actions and reactions, so shall you be a victim. Understand that the physical world is a learning environment created by the beings that inhabit it, and everything that occurs in it serves a learning purpose.

My intention in this book has been to help you create a safe environment for yourself and your loved ones. In addition, I want you to grow into the person you have been designed to be.

When we align our thoughts, emotions, and actions with the highest parts of ourselves, we are filled with enthusiasm, purpose, and meaning. Life becomes rich and abundant. We have no thoughts of regret, no feeling of fear. Becoming fully in tune with our world lets us experience the blissful feeling of authentic power.

In our society, people are filled with fear of the unknown. That fear is wasted energy. I challenge you to become more in tune with your individual strengths. Taking control of your personal security is the first step in this process. Once you know that you can make a decision capable of saving your own life, every other decision in life becomes relatively simple.

I'll leave you with the phrase that my parents, Bob and Judy, always said to me: Be good, behave, and be careful, and no matter what happens I know you can handle it.

Have faith, stay safe!

—Robert L. Siciliano

"THE LIFESAVER"

About the Author

Robert L. Siciliano, "THE LIFESAVER," is president of The Safety Minute Seminars Company, which is based in Boston, Massachusetts. He is a professional speaker, trainer, consultant, and media personality on the topic of personal security. His background includes various martial arts, Model Mugging, kickboxing, night club security, and street confrontation.

He is a much sought-after keynote speaker and seminar leader for major corporations and associations throughout North America.

See Robert on-line at www.safetyminute.com or call him direct at 1-800-2-GET SAFE.

**Attitude is a little thing
that makes a big difference.**

Index

Robert L. Siciliano Live

"THE LIFESAVER"

Combining humor, powerful anecdotes, and bullet points of unforgettable tips and techniques, Robert Siciliano's presentations give listeners immediately applicable real-world information to change attitudes and behaviors. The effectiveness of his work converts listeners' energy into increased productivity that benefits both individuals and their employers.

The Safety Minute Seminars Company offers a variety of programs and training opportunities to individuals, associations, and corporations worldwide, as well as audio and video programs based on the principles in this book.

To have Robert speak at your convention or meeting or to receive more information about any of the Safety Minute products, please call or write:

The Safety Minute Seminars Company
P.O. Box 15145
Boston, MA 02215
Tel: 800-2-GET SAFE
Fax: 877-2-FAX NOW

Quantity Sales

This book is available at special discounts when purchased in bulk by companies, organizations, and special interest groups. Custom imprinting, logos, or excerpting can also be accommodated to fit special needs. For details, please call or write:

Safety Zone Press
P. O. Box 15145
Boston, MA 02215
Tel: 800-2-GET SAFE (243-8723)
Fax: 877-2-FAX NOW (232-9669)

YOU CAN PROTECT YOURSELF!

"Living on High Alert- How to Guard Your Safety & Security"

When President Bush told all Americans to be on "high alert," he reinforced the message that Speaker and author Robert Siciliano has been carrying throughout the USA for more than a decade. To increase security and reduce liability, consider the solution that is so effective, so well-thought of, these major media offered it to their audiences.

Featured on **CNN, MSNBC, FOX News, Montel Williams, Maury Povich, Sally Jesse Raphael, David Brenner, Howard Stern, and in RealtyTimes.com,** *Woman's Day, Good Housekeeping, Mademoiselle & The NY Post*

Millions of viewers and subscribers have already learned the secrets of personal safety and security developed by one man. His skills have benefited thousands more through presentations to Coldwell Banker, Century 21, KPMG Peat Marwick, Digital Equipment Corporation, the Women's Council of Realtors, the Public Schools in Massachusetts, and Licensed Practical Nurses of Massachusetts Inc., among others. Known as "The Lifesaver," this man is safety expert Robert L. Siciliano, a certified safety instructor for Massachusetts health-care workers and a highly praised consultant.

He can bring the same benefits to your organization. It takes only a few hours, and your organization will find the process fun and light-hearted.

We are not selling fear. The statistics speak for themselves. Robert offers a solution to an ongoing problem. Here's an overview of the seminars to benefit you and your organization:

MEMBER

Seminar Topics

Safe Travel Security

The Problem: Risk management and international security are of considerable concern. Hijackers and terrorists are causing travelers to lose sleep post-9/11.

The Solution: Incorporate intelligence and information, pre-planning and prevention and response training into your travel agenda.

Workplace Violence

The Problem: Violence in the workplace has become an epidemic, causing nightmares for corporations. Anyone who believes "It can't happen here" surely is mistaken.

The Solution: Create an environment in which employees are safe, secure, happy, and productive. Put systems in place that head off violence and foster prediction and prevention.

Personal Safety and Success

The Problem: Some believe that sex and violence on TV, in movies and in video games are the problem. Others believe that poverty, welfare, and single parent-fatherless homes are the cause. The fact is that drugs, alcohol, mental illness, and combinations of these all contribute to violence in America.

The Solution: Take responsibility for your safety and your family's safety. A one-to three-hour seminar on Personal Safety is actually a fun and entertaining experience. Learn the fundamentals of security in a positive and motivating environment. You have all the ingredients to protect your family and business, we just give you the recipe.

ID Theft Security

The Problem: A day will come when almost everyone knows somebody who has been affected by this crime. Over 750,000 people found themselves affected last year and thousands more don't even know they were hit.

The Solution: It lies with you. Ignorance and naiveté on your part will surely ruin all your years of hard work at maintaining a good credit rating - unless you take the time to protect yourself against the horrors of ID Theft.

Anti-Terror Security on Premises

The Problem: Terrorism, a frightening enemy, the unknown, an unseen enemy. Predators live among us, and hide suddenly striking where and when we least expect it. Business owners are scrambling to secure their working environments.

The Solution: Systems and strategies to prevent attacks at your place of business. Know what your options are and incorporate the fundamentals of premises security into your daily functions.

Identity Fraud – A Bigger Threat Than Identity Theft

 Your personal information is a thief's best friend. Fraudsters can take your Social Security number, link a new name to it, run up bills on your credit cards or start to steal your identity through Internet directories.

IdentitySweep Notifies You BEFORE the Crime Occurs!

IdentitySweep alerts you to identity fraud, using proprietary, leading-edge technology to conduct an extensive sweep through thousands of databases, searching for your SSN and then tracking suspicious changes.

Credit Reports Will Not Protect Victims from Identity Fraud

Identity fraud is untrackable by traditional solutions, like the credit bureaus.

A credit report only notifies a victim after it's too late – and they don't show accounts opened with a victim's SSN using a different name. Stolen credit card activity can take up to three months to show up on your report. And credit bureaus don't monitor Web directories

Identity Sweep gives you Comprehensive 3-way Protection

1. Alerts you to name or Social Security number alterations
2. Sends 24/7 alerts if your credit card is stolen or in play on the Web
3. Deletes personal information from Web directories – name, address, telephone, even email!

Subscribe and receive reports within minutes
http://www.identitysweep.com – only $4.95/month!

 **PROTECT & MANAGE** your identity 24/7

Identity Protection and Prevention

Detect identity theft/mistaken identity *BEFORE* it destroys your life!

Your public records are the key to staying on top of identity theft and avoiding the devastating consequences of mistaken identity. Order a Public Information Profile from MyPublicInfo and take control of your identity.

The PIP searches over 9,000 data sources to summarize: Criminal records, bankruptcy records, liens and judgments, insurance claims, address and telephone histories, real estate transactions (even aerial photos of your house!), professional licenses, motor-vehicle registrations, unclaimed assets, etc. – and more!

You PIP will pinpoint possible cases of mistaken identity that might cost you your next job or that mortgage on your dream house. **There is no other source for this information!**

Your PIP will:

- Detect early identity theft and mistaken identity.
- Show you information not found in any credit
  report or anywhere else.
- Put you on equal footing with employers, snoopers, and ID thieves.
- Mistaken identity is a growing problem with
  devastating consequences, and **the PIP is the
  only solution!**

Order your PIP today!
Go to http://www.mypublicinfo.com
Click "Order"
Choose "Promotional Discount" from "Promotion"
Use Promo Code "SafetyMinute10"

Do you know who you're dealing with?
Find out instantly!

Are you concerned about your family's safety? Do you ever wonder if someone is hiding their criminal background? TrueScoop gives you confidence about people who are in contact with your family, like a coach, contractor, date, teacher, nanny or coworker.

Now you can check out anyone who comes in contact with your family. TrueScoop gives you the power to make informed decisions, detailing criminal, misdemeanor, and felony records nationwide...right down to eye color.

TRUESCOOP:

- Keeps your family safe with criminal and sex-offender searches
- Free check in the nationwide sex offender database
- Most comprehensive - 227+ million records
- Coverage in all 50 states.
- **No other criminal background check gives you all this!**

Easy to order for only $19.95

Go to http://www.truescoop.info and get instant peace of mind.

TrueScoop comes with a 200% money-back guarantee, so start protecting yourself and your family today.